Farm Labor in the United States

Farm Labor in the United States

EDITED BY C. E. BISHOP

COLUMBIA UNIVERSITY PRESS

New York and London

Charles Edwin Bishop is Head of the Department of Economics and Executive Director of the Agricultural Policy Institute at North Carolina State University. Mr. Bishop is coauthor of *Introduction to Agricultural Economic Analysis.*
The research reported herein was financed through the programs of the Office of Manpower Policy, Evaluation, and Research, United States Department of Labor.

First printing 1967
Second printing 1968

Library of Congress Catalog Card Number: 66-28037
Printed in the United States of America

Preface

Technological progress in American agriculture has resulted in greatly increased productivity of farm labor and in a sharp reduction in the number of farm workers. These effects, however, have not been uniformly distributed among regions and types of farms. Consequently, two of the current major concerns with respect to farm labor are the improvement of the persistently low return for labor services in farming and maintenance of an adequate supply of farm labor to carry out farm operations, particularly in types of farming which have not been mechanized. These objectives might be achieved relatively easily by substantially increasing the farm wage rate except for the fact that for many years the United States has been pursuing a low-cost food policy and that it has an agriculture consisting predominantly of family-operated farms. On many of these farms the return received by the operator and his family for labor services is less than that received by hired farm workers.

The low returns for farm manpower in the United States are due in part from the fact that this nation has never developed an explicit manpower policy for agriculture. Instead, farm manpower has been exempted from much of the major labor legislation. Primary emphasis in agricultural policies and programs has been placed on product markets and product market conditions. In the factor markets, land use and conservation policies have been developed and farmers have been provided with subsidies to encourage them to make specified uses of land. Special credit programs have been developed to encourage farmers to make particular types of investments. Vocational education and training have been provided for practically all farm youth desiring such programs, but these education and training programs have been highly oriented toward farming and farm-related occupations with little reference to nonfarm employment opportunities and to manpower policy.

In view of the rapid changes occurring in the structure of agriculture and of the importance of occupational and geographic mobility to a solution to the low-income problems in rural America, there is a need to relate manpower policy for agriculture more explicitly to national manpower policy and to general economic goals. To this end the Office of Manpower Policy, Evaluation and Research sponsored a conference on farm manpower in Washington, D. C., October 28 to 29, 1965. The papers contained in this monograph provided the background for discussion of farm manpower problems and policies at the conference.

C. E. BISHOP

Raleigh, North Carolina

July, 1966

Contents

Farm Labor in the United States

[1]

Dimensions of the Farm Labor Problem

C. E. BISHOP

Unquestionably, the most significant aspect of the farm labor problem is the persistently low return for labor services in farming. Although there is substantial variation among states and regions of the United States, the return for labor services in farming is lower than the return in nonfarm employment in all major regions.[1]

It should not be inferred from these findings, however, that all farm families have low incomes or that the return is low for all farm labor. In 1963 more than 27 percent of the three and one-half million farms in the United States sold more than $10,000 of farm products (Table 1). The average net income of these farm operator families, including income from off-farm sources, was greater than the average for all families in the United States. Nevertheless, recent studies which attempt to adjust the farm and nonfarm labor returns for differences such as those in age, sex, education, and skill components suggest that even after standardization of these factors the return for labor services in agriculture remains 30 to 40 percent less than the return for comparable labor in nonfarm occupations.[2] In short, there

---

C. E. BISHOP is Executive Director of the Agricultural Policy Institute, North Carolina State University, Raleigh, N. C.

[1] D. Gale Johnson, "Functioning of the Labor Market," *Journal of Farm Economics,* Vol. XXXIII, February 1951, pp. 75-86. C. E. Bishop, "Underemployment of Labor in Southeastern Agriculture," *Journal of Farm Economics,* Vol. XXXVI, May 1954, pp. 258-72.

[2] D. Gale Johnson, "Labor Mobility and Agricultural Adjustment," *Agricultural Adjustment Problems in a Growing Economy,* Iowa State University Press, 1958, pp. 163-72. D. E. Hathaway, *Government and Agriculture,* Macmillan, 1963, p. 35. It should be recognized that manpower is delivered in the form of people and that since wages are based predominantly on the inputs

is a substantial incentive to transfer from farm to nonfarm occupations, and vast numbers transfer each year. Since 1940 there has been a net transfer of more than 25 million persons from farm to nonfarm residences in the United States.[3] Millions more have turned to part-time farming and multiple-job holding. In spite of this transfer the gap in earnings of manpower persists.

Through employment and wage policies, immigration controls, public policies concerning education, and in many other ways government has long influenced geographic and occupational transfers of manpower. Until recently, however, the transfer of manpower from farms was largely unstructured and was influenced primarily through indirect actions rather than through policies designed specifically to enhance or to impede a reduction in farm manpower. This chapter presents the dimensions of the farm problem in broad outline in the hope that a better understanding of forces affecting the supply of and demand for manpower in farming and of the factors causing and

Table 1 Distribution of Farms by Value of Sales and Income, United States, 1963

Farms with Sales	*No. of Farms (000)*	*Distribution of Farms (percent)*	*Income per Farm Operator Family*		
			Realized Net Income	*Off-Farm Income*	*Total* [a]
$20,000 and over	384	10.7	$10,180	$2,177	$12,357
10,000 to 19,999	594	16.6	6,207	1,512	7,719
5,000 to 9,999	609	17.0	3,731	1,778	5,509
2,500 to 4,999	463	13.0	2,337	2,080	4,417
Less than 2,500	1,523	42.7	1,029	3,222	4,251
Part-time	903	25.3	919	4,450	5,369
Part-retirement	418	11.7	1,086	1,880	2,966
Other	202	5.7	1,406	510	1,916
All farms	3,573	100.0	3,504	2,431	5,935

[a] Includes nonmoney income from farm food and housing.
Source: USDA, *Farm Income Situation,* November 1964.

of people rather than on manpower per se the characteristics of the people themselves will affect employability.

[3] V. J. Banks et al., *Farm Population—Estimates for 1910–62,* ERS-130, USDA, 1963, and *Farm Population—Estimates for 1964,* ERS-233, 1965.

perpetuating disequilibria in the returns for labor services may provide the basis for the development of effective farm manpower policy.

FARM MANPOWER NEEDS AND TECHNOLOGICAL CHANGE

Farm manpower needs are determined by the market conditions for farm products and the relative productivities of manpower and other resources in producing farm products. At the high per capita incomes prevailing in the United States there is little inclination to purchase additional food when income increases or when the prices of foods decline. Moreover, the demand elasticities are relatively low in Western Europe and in other major commercial markets for United States farm products. The rate of growth in the demand for United States farm products in major commercial markets, therefore, is determined largely by increases in population, and the demand is increasing slowly.

Since the mid 1930s technological innovations in United States agriculture have been occurring at a very rapid pace, and the most important determinant of manpower needs in farming has been changes in the technology used in producing farm commodities. Two aspects of technological improvements that are particularly relevant to manpower needs in farming are the resource substitution effects and the firm size effects generated by technological improvement.

For the most part, technological innovations in agriculture have not been neutral in their effects on the demand for resources. Rather, most innovations have altered relative resource productivities in such a way as to provide incentives to change the resource mix employed. Early innovations in agriculture were largely of a biological, chemical, or mechanical nature.[4] Typically, these improvements in technology increased the productivity of capital and altered the technical rates of substitution of capital for manpower, reducing the amount of capital which was necessary to replace a unit of manpower at particular levels of output. Many of these innovations also altered the rates

[4] E. O. Heady, "Basic Economic and Welfare Aspects of Farm Technological Advance," *Journal of Farm Economics,* Vol. XXXI, May 1949, pp. 293-316.

of substitution of manpower and land, making it possible to reduce the amount of manpower in relation to land needed to produce specified levels of output. Technological innovations, therefore, have provided strong incentives to increase the use of capital and to decrease the use of manpower and to a lesser extent the use of land in the production of farm commodities.[5]

There is a second major effect of changes in farm production technology. Typically, technological innovations decrease the cost of producing additional output, thereby increasing the most profitable level of output for the firm. Since most innovations provide incentives to expand output at the firm level, the size effects are in the direction of increased use of manpower.

Technological improvements affect size and manpower use in yet another way. The increases in investment and in the size of operation which are accompanied by technological improvements generally lead to a greater degree of production specialization and to changes in the organizational structure of agricultural industries. These organizational improvements may occur within the firm as a result of resource recombination and greater specialization or they may occur through vertical or horizontal integration among firms. In either case organizational improvements tend to decrease the amount of manpower used for specified levels of output. In effect, therefore, organizational changes also lead to a substitution of other resources for manpower.

In summary, the technological changes which have been taking place in agriculture have provided incentives to substitute capital for manpower and to increase the size of farm firms. At the firm level, the substitution effects tend to decrease the demand for manpower whereas the size effects tend to increase the demand for manpower. Because of the slow rate of growth in farm product demand, however, prices fall rapidly as aggregate output expands. Under these conditions the only way for the size effects to be fully realized at the firm level is through a reduction in the number of firms. In the aggregate, therefore, the substitution effects between capital and manpower exceed the size effects, with a consequent sharp reduction in the em-

[5] Recent innovations also have made it possible to reduce the amount of capital needed for given levels of output. Even so, these innovations have provided further incentives to substitute capital for manpower in the production of farm commodities.

ployment of manpower in farming. Thus farm people have been forced to choose between (1) massive transfers of manpower to nonfarm occupations in an effort to increase the return for the manpower remaining in farming or (2) occupational immobility, large-scale underemployment, and sharply reduced returns for manpower in farming.

Since the late 1930s, the processes of adjustment outlined above have been taking place very rapidly in United States agriculture. Even so, the adjustments have not been completed, or are they likely to be completed in the near future. They are not once-and-over changes. As economic development occurs, capital is accumulated, and it becomes relatively low priced in comparison to manpower. Under these conditions research tends to be oriented in the direction of creating new technology which increases the rate of substitution of capital for manpower.[6] The decrease in the demand for manpower in farming, therefore, is a normal complement of economic growth and should be expected to continue.

A MASSIVE EXODUS OF MANPOWER FROM FARMING

Since 1920 there has been a massive exodus of manpower from farms in the United States.[7] Gross migration probably was two to three times as large as net migration during this period. However, the effects have not been uniformly distributed among regions, and, in spite of this vast migration, the return for labor in farming remains comparatively low.

By 1950 the adjustments which had been effected in the agriculture of the Corn Belt and of the West were large enough to have achieved roughly a parity of returns for farm and nonfarm labor services in those regions. In the meantime, the South and New England lagged behind. During the decade of the 1950s, however, technological improvements occurred rapidly in farming, and the returns for farm manpower in the Corn Belt and in the West degenerated relative to

[6] J. R. Hicks, *The Theory of Wages,* The Macmillan Company, 1932, Chapter 6.

[7] V. J. Banks et al., *Farm Population.*

the returns for comparable manpower in nonfarm employment in those regions. By 1960 in all major regions the returns for farm manpower were substantially less than the returns for comparable manpower in nonfarm employment.

As a result of rapid and extensive technological innovations in American agriculture during the 1950s, the labor market was unable to effect sufficient manpower transfers to prevent a deterioration in the relative return for farm manpower. If the factor markets functioned perfectly, agricultural innovation would be accompanied by a transfer of manpower from farm to nonfarm employment until wage differences were eliminated except for costs of transfer, costs of acquisition of skills, and differences represented in heterogeneity of manpower resources, or in employment and living conditions. In spite of the mass transfer of manpower from agriculture, the gap in earnings of labor in farm and nonfarm employment has not been closed. Furthermore, the supply of farm manpower is so large relative to the demand that since 1950 earnings of farm manpower have increased at a slower rate than increases in labor productivity.[8]

IMPEDIMENTS TO MOBILITY

The reasons for the failure of the labor market to transfer sufficient quantities of manpower from farms to bring about equality of returns for resources should be found in the conditions of supply of manpower to nonfarm employment or the conditions of demand for this manpower. Numerous factors could conceivably reduce the elasticity of supply of manpower from farms to nonfarm employment.

The United States economy has been characterized by a strong element of agricultural fundamentalism, which has been an important influence in the development of public policies and programs affecting agriculture. It manifests itself in the many special considerations given to agriculture and to particular segments of agriculture. Some of these considerations impede mobility and structural change.[9]

[8] L. B. Jones and J. W. Christian, "Some Observations on the Agricultural Labor Market," *Industrial and Labor Relations Review*, Vol. 18, No. 4, July 1965, pp. 522-34.

[9] W. D. Diehl, *Farm-Nonfarm Migration in the Southeast: A Costs Returns Analysis*, Ph.D. dissertation, North Carolina State University, Raleigh, N.C., 1964, p. 30.

Farming, moreover, has traditionally been viewed as a "superior" occupation by farm families. They have encouraged their sons and daughters to become farmers. For example, a recent study on the lifetime occupational mobility of males shows that 82 percent of the farmers and farm managers in the United States in 1962 had fathers who were farmers and farm managers whereas 60 percent of the farm laborers and foremen had fathers in that occupational group.[10] Even though there is a high probability that the fathers of persons engaged in farm employment in the United States were also engaged in farm employment, the occupational inheritance of farmers and farm managers is only moderately high (Table 2). One in six of the sons of farmers and farm managers are currently in the same occupations as their fathers; the remainder are scattered over various occupational groups. The sons of farm laborers and foremen are less likely to remain in agriculture than are the sons of farmers and farm managers. Even so, occupational inheritance is excessive in farming, and more sons remain on farms than can expect to make a reasonable living from farming.

Farm youth also are handicapped by the limited opportunities which have been provided them for nonagricultural vocational training. A very high percentage of the male farm youth in secondary schools are enrolled in courses in vocational agriculture.[11] In 1960 there were approximately 600 thousand rural farm males of high school age, and fewer than 90 percent of them were enrolled in high school. In the same year there were 464 thousand males enrolled in vocational agriculture. Since some youth who enroll in vocational agriculture courses obviously drop out of school, the number of farm youth with some training in vocational agriculture in 1960 who were of high school age at that time obviously exceeded 464 thousand. Clearly, a very high percentage of the rural farm males attending high school receive some training in vocational agriculture.

A rather high percentage of those receiving training in vocational agriculture have entered farming as a career. A compilation of the results of studies analyzing the occupations of former vocational agri-

[10] *Current Population Report, Lifetime Occupational Mobility of Adult Males,* March 1962, Series P-23, No. 11, May 1964.

[11] C. E. Bishop and G. S. Tolley, "Migration in Farming and Related Occupations," *Education for a Changing World of Work,* Appendix II, OE-80025, U. S. Department of Health, Education, and Welfare, 1963.

Table 2 Current Occupation by Father's Occupation—Noninstitutional Male Population 25–65 Years Old for the United States: March 1962

Father's Occupation (Percent Distribution)	*Total Population 25–64 Years Old*	*Current Occupation*									
		Professional, Tech., and Kindred Workers	*Managers, Officials, and Proprietors, Except Farm*	*Sales Workers*	*Clerical and Kindred Workers*	*Craftsmen, Foremen, and Kindred Workers*	*Operatives and Kindred Workers*	*Service Workers, incl. Private Household*	*Laborers Except Farm and Mine*	*Farmers and Farm Managers*	*Farm Laborers and Foremen*
Total	100.0	12.5	16.1	5.0	6.6	20.7	18.9	5.9	6.9	5.6	1.8
Professional, tech., and kindred workers	100.0	41.0	17.5	9.0	6.9	8.7	10.3	3.1	2.0	1.8	0.4
Managers, officials, and proprietors, exc. farm	100.0	21.6	34.1	9.1	7.1	13.8	8.5	2.5	1.9	1.0	0.3
Sales workers	100.0	19.5	30.0	15.0	6.2	11.9	10.4	3.2	2.1	1.7	0.1
Clerical and kindred workers	100.0	28.0	17.8	7.8	9.6	16.9	9.2	6.0	3.0	1.3	0.0
Craftsmen, foremen, and kindred workers	100.0	13.0	16.5	4.7	7.8	29.4	17.5	5.1	4.8	0.8	0.4
Operatives and kindred workers	100.0	11.7	12.2	4.4	6.6	23.8	25.9	5.9	7.5	0.9	0.9
Service workers, incl. private household	100.0	10.0	14.2	5.7	9.5	21.0	21.0	11.1	6.3	1.0	0.2
Laborers, except farm and mine	100.0	5.9	8.0	3.6	8.0	22.5	26.3	9.1	14.1	1.2	1.1
Farmers and farm mgrs.	100.0	5.3	11.5	2.5	4.7	10.7	20.5	5.2	8.5	17.8	4.3
Farm laborers and foremen	100.0	2.3	7.5	2.0	3.8	20.5	26.0	8.1	13.4	6.2	10.2
Occupation not reported	100.0	8.6	14.0	3.6	6.6	20.3	21.3	10.4	10.9	2.3	1.7

Source: Current Population Reports, Series P-23, No. 11, May 12, 1964.

The population in this report includes 718,000 members of the Armed Forces living off post or with their families on post; all other members of the Armed Forces are excluded. Excluded also are those not in experienced civilian labor force.

culture students between 1918 and 1960 shows "that one third of the former students were farming and approximately 8 percent were employed in farm related occupations when the studies were made." [12] A study of students who were graduated since World War II gave similar results.

A recent Iowa study indicates that 39 percent of the farm boys who were graduated from high school in 1959 planned a career in farming. Such a high proportion of farm youth cannot be employed efficiently in farming. There is little question that more youth aspire to careers in farming than the industry can accommodate with reasonable returns for labor and management services.

The direct costs of transfer also may serve as an impediment to occupational mobility. Farm to nonfarm manpower transfers frequently involve geographic mobility as well as occupational mobility. The direct costs of moving depend on the size of the family, the amount of property moved, the distance, and the method of transportation. One study reports on the costs of moving from one labor market to another in the United States in 1962 and 1963.[13] The average cost of moving for people other than those who were transferred by their employer was $180. The cost of moving was less for younger age groups. Three-fourths of those who were under 25 years of age moved for less than $50. For 83 percent of the movers, costs were less than 10 percent of a year's income. Although there are many nonpecuniary costs involved in geographic mobility, the direct costs probably are not sufficient to serve as a major impediment to migration.

Migration from farms has been highly selective with respect to age and with respect to education. The young, who have less invested in agriculture, also have better nonfarm opportunities and a longer period of prospective employment in which to recoup the costs of migration. They, therefore, are much more prone to transfer to nonfarm occupations. An age cohort analysis by Tolley and Hjort shows that, although there is considerable variation among regions of the United States in projected migration rates by age, in all regions a very high

[12] *Ibid.*, p. 24.

[13] *The Cost of Geographic Mobility*, Area Redevelopment Administration, U. S. Department of Commerce, 1964.

rate of transfer is expected for persons in the 15 to 24 age group (Table 3). This high rate of transfer emphasizes the need for nonfarm vocational skills if these young people are to avoid becoming a part of the large number of unemployed youth.

Clearly the major avenue through which the supply of farm man-

Table 3 Projections to 1970 for Males Remaining on Farms and Migrating off Farms

Age in 1960	*Number of 1960 Rural Farm Males Surviving to 1970*	*Number Expected to be Rural Farm Males in 1970*	*Implied Off-Farm Migration*	*Percent Migrating*
		(*in thousands*)		
		United States		
5–14	1,542	631	911	59.0
15–24	985	259	726	73.7
25–34	566	436	130	23.0
35–44	750	629	118	15.7
45–65	1,287	1,140	150	11.7
	5,130	3,095	2,035	39.7
		Northeast		
5–14	99	47	52	52.5
15–24	66	29	36	54.5
25–34	43	38	5	11.6
35–44	54	46	7	13.0
45–65	86	74	14	16.3
	348	234	114	32.8
		North Central		
5–14	610	268	342	56.1
15–24	367	139	228	62.1
25–34	241	219	22	9.1
35–44	319	288	31	9.7
45–65	533	493	41	7.7
	2,070	1,407	664	32.1
		South, white		
5–14	470	188	282	60.0
15–24	338	59	279	82.5
25–34	178	112	66	37.1
35–44	248	194	53	21.4
45–65	457	414	44	9.6
	1,691	967	724	42.8

Age in 1960	*Number of 1960 Rural Farm Males Surviving to 1970*	*Number Expected to be Rural Farm Males in 1970*	*Implied Off-Farm Migration*	*Percent Migrating*
		(in thousands)		
		South, nonwhite		
5–14	221	70	151	68.3
15–24	131	8	124	94.7
25–34	49	21	28	57.0
35–44	55	37	17	30.9
45–65	93	67	26	28.0
	549	203	346	63.0
		West		
5–14	142	58	84	59.2
15–24	83	24	59	71.1
25–34	55	46	9	16.4
35–44	74	64	10	13.5
45–65	118	92	25	21.2
	472	284	187	39.6

Source: C. E. Bishop and G. S. Tolley, "Manpower in Farming and Related Occupations," *Education for a Changing World of Work,* OE-80025, U.S. Department of Health, Education, and Welfare, 1963. The estimates were based on a method developed by G. S. Tolley and H. W. Hjort, "Age Mobility and Southern Skill—Looking Ahead for Area Development," *Journal of Farm Economics,* Vol. XLV, February 1963, pp. 31–46.

power is determined is through conditions affecting the entry of youth into farm occupations. In spite of the high rate of exodus, the rate of entry into farming still is considerably in excess of the number of new farming opportunities created which can yield a return for labor services equal to the return received in nonfarm employment.

In an earlier study I suggested an alternative hypothesis that the supply of labor to nonfarm firms is highly elastic with respect to prevailing relative rates of return in farm and nonfarm employment.[14] There is no doubt that considerable manpower can be transferred from farm to nonfarm employment at prevailing farm and nonfarm rates of return for labor services. In my judgment the actual rate of

[14] C. E. Bishop, "Economic Aspects of Changes in the Farm Labor Force," Chapter 4 in *Labor Mobility and Population in Agriculture,* Iowa State University Press, 1961, p. 40.

migration is determined largely by shifts in the demand for manpower in nonfarm employment.

Changes in farm population through migration and reclassification of residence since 1920 are shown in Figure 1. After the sharp drop in farm prices in 1920 there was a large transfer from farms. The transfer decreased in size throughout the remainder of the 1920s and early 1930s, and remained fairly stable throughout the remainder of the 1930s. The pattern since 1940 has been much more variable, but the trend has been downward.

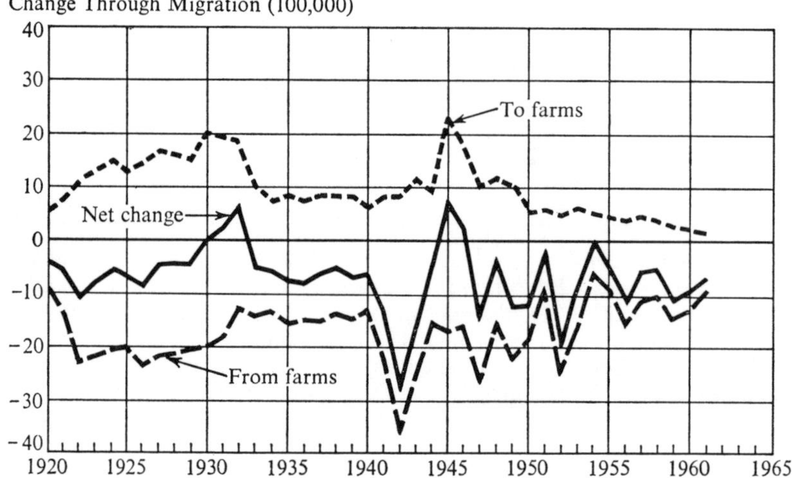

Figure 1. Change in farm population through migration and reclassification of residence. Source: *Farm Population,* ERS, USDA.

The transfer in the opposite direction, from nonfarm to farm residences, shows three different trends over time. Throughout the 1920s the trend was upward. After a sharp decline in the early 1930s the trend was rather stable through the early 1940s. Since the adjustments following World War II the trend has been downward and rather steady.

An earlier analysis emphasized the significance of the level of unemployment to migration and concluded that during periods when unemployment was above 5 percent the number of job openings in occupations for which migrants qualify is a major factor limiting migration. During such periods farm people are willing to migrate to nonfarm areas in large numbers without an increase in relative payments for labor services in nonfarm employment.[15] On the other hand, when the level of unemployment in the economy was below the 5 percent level, the migration of farm people to nonfarm residences increased as the nonfarm wage rate increased relative to returns for labor services in farming.

A similar hypothesis was set forth recently by Jones and Christian. They concluded that the principal causal factor for the low wage rates in United States agriculture was "the redundant supply of labor in agriculture, a condition which . . . is perpetuated by lack of opportunity in alternative occupations. Agricultural labor is 'trapped' in the 'other America.' "[16]

Other supporting evidence for the deficiency of demand for manpower hypothesis is obtained by looking at the distribution of migrants over occupations. Sjaastad shows that more than 70 percent of the workers who transfer from farm to nonfarm occupations are employed in the blue-collar occupations—craftsmen and foremen, operatives and kindred workers, and laborers other than farm.[17] Furthermore, there is some indication that the percentage of migrants from farms entering these occupations has been increasing over time.[18] These, of course, are the occupational categories in which unemployment has been greatest. Jones and Christian emphasized that the competition confronting agricultural workers in search of alternative employment is most severe where employment opportunities seem to them to be greatest.[19]

The excellent work of Perkins and Hathaway provides us with a greater insight into the effects of unemployment upon occupational

[15] *Ibid.*

[16] Jones and Christian, *Industrial and Labor Relations Review*, p. 523.

[17] L. A. Sjaastad, "Occupational Structure and Migration Patterns," *Labor Mobility and Population in Agriculture*, Iowa State University Press, 1961, p. 21.

[18] C. E. Bishop, "Agriculture and a Full Employment Economy," Agriculture Experiment Station Bulletin 556, Virginia Polytechnic Institute, 1964.

[19] B. B. Perkins, *Labor Mobility between the Farm and Nonfarm Sector*, Ph.D. dissertation, Michigan State University, East Lansing, Michigan, 1964, p. 114.

transfers. Whereas most mobility studies have been concerned with geographic migration, the Perkins and Hathaway study deals with industry changes. They provide the best information to date on the transfer from nonfarm to farm employment. There is a substantial difference between gross and net migration. The ratio of net to gross migration is sometimes taken as an indication of the efficiency of migration. Even if mobility were perfect, there could be a significant transfer of people to rural areas. Nevertheless, the flow of people from nonfarm to farm occupations in the United States is large enough to be a cause of concern. The impact of the backflow on the farm labor force is emphasized in Perkins' conclusion that "if in-farm mobility had been zero during the years 1956–59, the annual average reduction in the size of the farm labor force would have been 15.8 percent instead of 3.6 percent. Even if those who moved back into agriculture after only a year in the nonfarm sector had stayed in that sector the net off-farm mobility rate would have been nearly doubled." [20] A better system of guidance of manpower transfers from farm to nonfarm occupations could contribute greatly to more efficient use of manpower.

Improvement in the returns for farm labor services also is hindered by impediments to structural change in agriculture. The structural changes which are implied by agricultural development are often extensive, and many rigidities are encountered. The major impact of technological change has been on consolidation of farms. The average age of operators of farms selling less that $5,000 of farm products in 1959 was 50 years, 4 years more than for farms selling $10,000 or more of products.[21] It is widely known that unemployment is high among the older age groups and that the difficulty of transferring among occupations increases with age. The problems of structural readjustments within agriculture, therefore, are interrelated with the problems of obtaining nonfarm employment for persons in the older age groups.

Moreover, the land market like the labor market is far from perfect. Among the more important obstacles to the efficient transfer of land are (1) the immobility of manpower, (2) the high premium placed on land ownership in rural communities, (3) the capital gains

[20] *Ibid.*

[21] *U. S. Census of Agriculture, 1959,* Vol. II, Chapter 11.

potential from land ownership, resulting in part from farm price policies, (4) the low liquidity of investments in land in isolated areas, and (5) the lack of a well-conceived policy on agrarian structure.[22]

Structural changes also are complicated by the fact that mechanization has had differential effects among commodities and regions. The large seasonal differences in labor requirements in the production of farm commodities constitute an obstacle to labor mobility, especially for regions which depend heavily on monoculture of crops. Mechanization of farm production has done little to reduce peak manpower needs for some commodities. The productivity of labor services is very low in the production of some of these commodities, and the wage rate is correspondingly low. However, although the marginal productivity of manpower may be near zero during much of the year, during peak periods it is very high. The costs of not having sufficient manpower to meet peak needs, therefore, may be very high.

The lack of mechanized techniques of production to decrease manpower needs at peak periods undoubtedly is a factor which perpetuates low returns for labor services in agriculture. Very few areas have been able to develop an agriculture which provides reasonable incomes for farm families when the manpower is employed for only short periods of the year. In order to reduce underemployment, it has been necessary to mechanize the jobs with peak manpower requirements, thereby substituting capital for manpower, or to alter the product mix in such a way as to achieve less seasonal variation in the manpower input by providing employment for additional manpower during the slack periods.

MANPOWER POLICY BY DEFAULT

The low returns for farm manpower in the United States probably stem in part from the fact that this nation has never developed an explicit manpower policy for agriculture.[23] Instead, farm manpower

[22] J. Klotzman, *A Study of Obstacles to Shifts in the Use of Agricultural Land,* DAA-T-345, OECD, Paris, 1964, p. 10.

[23] C. E. Bishop, "Combating Rural Poverty," in *Our Stake in Commercial Agriculture, Rural Poverty and World Trade,* Center for Agricultural and Economic Development, Report No. 22, Iowa State University, Ames, Iowa, 1965.

has been exempted from most major labor legislation. Primary emphasis in agricultural policies and programs has been placed on product markets and product market conditions. In the factor market area, land use and conservation policies have been developed and farmers have been provided with subsidies to encourage them to make specified uses of land. Likewise, special credit programs have been developed to encourage farmers to make particular types of investments. As indicated above, vocational education and training have been provided for practically all farm youth desiring such programs, but these education and training programs have been highly oriented toward farming and farm-related occupations with little reference to nonfarm employment opportunities and to manpower policy.

In view of the changes now taking place and the importance of occupational and geographic mobility of labor to a solution of low-income problems in rural America, manpower policy for agriculture should be related explicitly to national manpower policy and to general economic goals. Increasing the mobility of manpower may or may not be a desirable part of such a policy. Certainly, mobility is not an end to be achieved as such. Instead, policies should be directed toward improving the mobility potential of manpower through training and through other programs in order to provide occupational and geographic flexibility and toward providing specific kinds of assistance to people to enable them to make and to carry out mobility decisions. As a minimum, farm manpower policy should seek to (1) gauge the employment potential in farming in terms of a reasonable return for manpower services, (2) provide counsel to individuals and families concerning income potentials in farm and nonfarm employment, (3) continue specialized training programs for those who are to continue as farmers, (4) expand nonfarm vocational training for those who have limited opportunities in farming, and (5) provide special counseling, guidance, and possibly relocation loans or grants to those who transfer to nonfarm occupations. The objective of these programs would be to increase the productivity of and returns for labor services. In the same way in which land-use policy has recognized that there are substantial differences in the productive potential and best uses of land, farm manpower policy would emphasize the differences in productive potential and adjustment capacity of farm people.

Finally, a farm manpower policy should include the development of an early warning system to detect changes in technology which are likely substantially to decrease farm manpower needs. Early detection of these changes and analysis of their probable magnitudes should make it possible to cushion the ensuing adjustments.

[2]

The Current Situation of the Hired Farm Labor Force

GLADYS K. BOWLES

This paper has two parts: (1) a section on the characteristics of hired farm workers, their employment and earnings from farm and nonfarm wage work in 1964, and related materials, to give a broad picture of the current socio-economic situation of the hired farm labor force, and (2) a section on the characteristics of the population of households with at least one person who did farm wage work in 1962, to provide relevant materials on the population dependent in varying degrees on hired farm work.

Source of Data on Hired Farm Workers. There are several federal sources of data on hired farm workers, and it should be pointed out that the various sets of data do not always show consistent trend patterns in numbers of workers, levels of wage rates, or annual earnings, even after survey coverage, sampling differences, and other methodological and conceptual matters are considered. Fortunately, the broad outlines of the socio-economic situation of hired farm workers are not obscured by the differences that appear among the various series, and references to such differences will be kept to a minimum in this chapter.

Most of the data utilized in this chapter come from annual surveys conducted by the Bureau of the Census for the Economic Research Service published in the series of reports relating to the hired farm working force.[1,2,3]

GLADYS K. BOWLES is Supervisory Statistician in the Economic Research Service of the U. S. Department of Agriculture.

[1] Gladys K. Bowles, *The Hired Farm Working Force of 1964: A Statistical*

HIRED FARM WORKERS

About 3.4 million persons in the civilian noninstitutional population 14 years old and over in December 1964 did some work on farms for cash wages or salary in 1964.[4]

Trends in Number of Hired Farm Workers. Averages for the 5-year periods, 1945–49 and 1960–64, from the hired farm worker series indicate that the number of persons who do farm wage work in the course of a year has not changed significantly. This is in contrast to the steady decline that has occurred among farm operators and unpaid family workers employed on farms. It is also in contrast to the trend shown by the U. S. Department of Agriculture series on hired farm employment,[5] which shows a decline of 20 percent in the annual average number of hired workers on farms between these two 5-year periods.

These differences in direction and the magnitude of change of these series are not necessarily inconsistent. The evidence from recent years points toward increasing seasonality in agricultural employment. Thus the number of people working during a year will tend to show a smaller change than annual averages based on employment for one week in each of the 12 months.

The hired farm working force is customarily very heterogeneous in

Report, Agricultural Economic Report 82, USDA, ERS, Washington, 1965. 30 pp.

[2] Gladys K. Bowles and Calvin L. Beale, *Characteristics of the Population of Hired Farm Worker Households,* Agricultural Economic Report 84, USDA, ERS, Washington, 1965. 21 pp.

[3] Gladys K. Bowles and Walter E. Sellers, Jr., *The Hired Farm Working Force of 1963 (with Supplementary Data for 1962),* Agricultural Economic Report 76, USDA, ERS, Washington, 1965. 63 pp.

[4] Not included in this 3.4 million are persons doing some farm wage work in 1964 who died, entered the Armed Forces, or were otherwise removed from the survey population by the time of the survey in December. For instance, most of the 200,000 foreign nationals admitted for agricultural work under contract in 1964 are excluded because they had returned to their homes prior to the time of the survey. The total number of persons who are excluded from the ERS survey probably does not exceed 500,000.

[5] U. S. Department of Agriculture, Statistical Reporting Service, *Farm Labor,* Crop Reporting Board, Washington, 1965. Various issues.

composition. In this discussion it will be helpful to distinguish several rather distinctive groups. One group is the *casual workers,* who do less than 25 days of farm wage work during a year; they totaled about 1.4 million persons in 1964. In the 5-year periods referred to earlier, casual workers increased by 27 percent. These short-time workers are mainly housewives, students, and others who are not in the labor force except for very short periods. A considerable proportion of them come from households whose principal source of income is from nonfarm work or from farming and who are generally at higher income levels than the groups who get their income primarily from farm wage work.

The second group, *noncasual workers,* totals about 2 million workers and is comprised of two major subgroups. The first subgroup includes about 650,000 regular and year-round workers. *Regular workers* are defined here as those who work for one or more farm employers for 150 to 249 days in a year; *year-round workers* are employed for 250 days or more. The second subgroup includes 1.3 million *seasonal workers* who work 25 to 149 days a year. Between 1945–49 and 1960–64 seasonal workers have averaged about the same in number; regular workers have declined about 10 percent. The biggest proportional decline has occurred among year-round workers where the number dropped nearly one-third.

Workers included in the Economic Research Service (ERS) survey did about 271 million man-days of work on farms, about one-fourth of the total number of days of labor on farms in 1964. Regular and year-round workers, who comprised about one-fifth of the hired farm working force, did about two-thirds of the total number of man-days of farm wage work. This is in contrast to the situation some 15 or 20 years ago, when these workers comprised about one-fourth of the hired farm working force and did about three-fourths of the man-days of work. Casual workers, who made up about two-fifths of the hired farm working force, did about 5 percent of the 271 million man-days of farm wage work (Figure 1).

Characteristics of Hired Farm Workers. About 71 percent of the 1964 hired farm working force were men and boys; about 69 percent were white. Only about a fourth were engaged chiefly in farm wage work. Over half, primarily housewives and students, were not in the

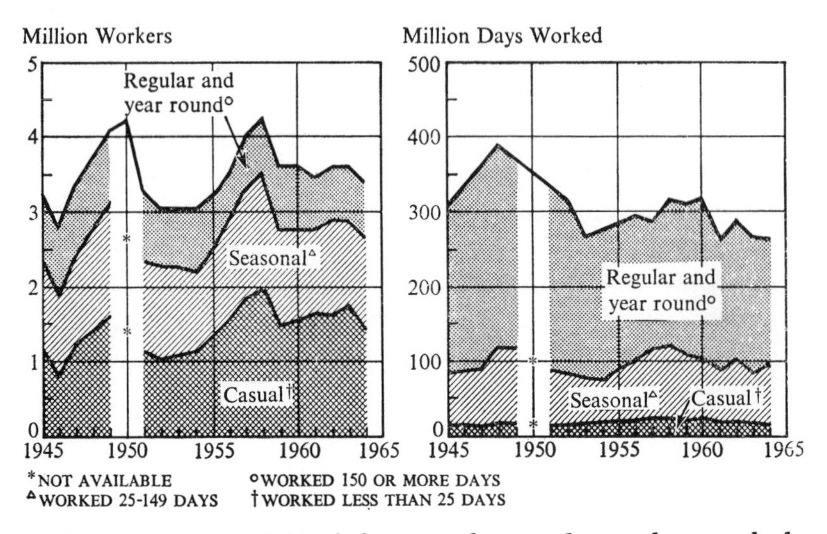

Figure 1. Number of hired farm workers and man-days worked. Source: ERS, USDA.

labor force most of the year; and even among noncasual workers, many were outside the labor force most of the year (Figure 2).

The hired farm working force is on the whole a relatively young group, having a median age of 25.3 years in 1964. Over one-fourth were young people 14 to 17 years old, who engage in farm work mainly in the summertime.

About 11 percent of the workers in the 1964 ERS survey did some farm wage work outside their home counties. These are usually called the domestic migratory workers, although a small proportion may actually be imported foreign workers.

Distribution of Workers. Nearly two-thirds of the 1964 hired farm working force lived in nonfarm places at the time of the survey in December, although some of them may have lived on farms at some time during the year. This is in contrast to the situation some years ago when approximately 65 percent lived on farms (Figure 3) at the time of year the ERS annual surveys were conducted.

In 1964 over half the workers lived in the South and about one-tenth in the Northeastern States. The remainder were located about equally in the North Central and Western States. The distribution of

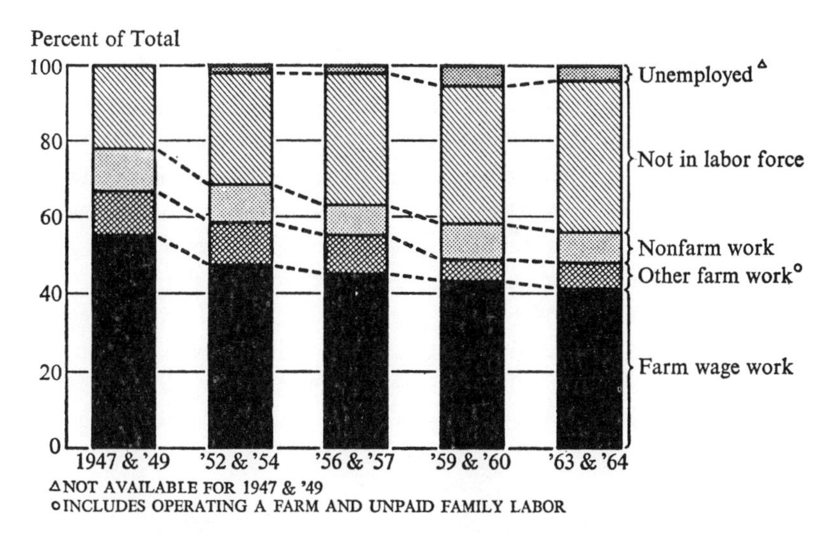

Figure 2. Chief activity of farm wage workers. Workers did 25 days or more of farm wage work during the year; average of selected years. Source: ERS, USDA.

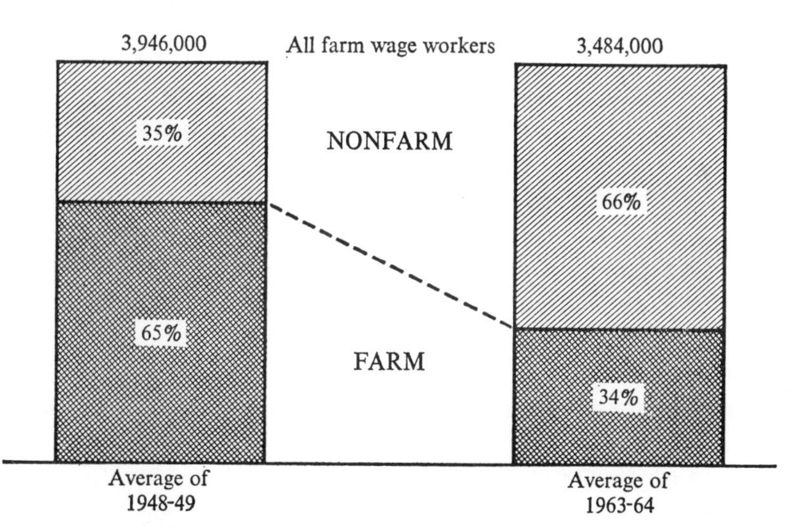

Figure 3. Residence of hired farm workers. Residence of farm wage workers in December of the reference years. Data relate to persons 14 years old and older in the civilian noninstitutional population who had done some farm wage work during the specified years. Source: ERS, USDA.

workers among the different regions has varied only slightly in recent years. Within these broad regions there are, however, widely diverse patterns in the proportions of farms which utilize any hired labor or in the use of regular and seasonal farm wage workers.

One of the striking features of the employment structure in agriculture is the heavy concentration of hired workers on a small proportion of the farms and in certain types of farming. Three states, California, Texas, and Florida, accounted for about one-third the total farm labor bill in 1964.[6] These states and North Carolina, New York, Illinois, Arkansas, Washington, Iowa, and Oregon accounted for about one-half the total farm labor bill in that year. According to the USDA series on farm employment, these states had about 47 percent of the annual average number of hired workers on farms in 1964.

Utilization of hired labor also varies extensively among types of farms. For instance, livestock and dairy farms usually have a comparatively high proportion of regular workers, as the stock require regular attention. Tobacco and cotton farms use few regular workers but rely heavily on seasonal workers. Fruit and nut farms and vegetable farms are also large users of seasonal hired workers, and they have also been the principal users of imported foreign workers in recent years. These specialty-product farms have been about the only users of the 36,000 foreign workers authorized by the Department of Labor in 1965. Citrus fruits, strawberries, apples, potatoes, shade tobacco, sugar cane, tomatoes, and some other specialty crops have utilized foreign workers at various periods in this year.

Geographic Mobility of Hired Workers. According to the latest report on mobility of the population published by the Bureau of the Census [7] (see also table below) male hired farm workers have the highest mobility rate of all civilian male wage and salary workers in major occupational groups. About 29 percent of male wage and salary farm workers lived in a different house in March 1964 from the house they lived in a year earlier. This percentage compares with

[6] U. S. Department of Agriculture, Economic Research Service, *Farm Income,* FIS 199, Supplement, Washington, August 1965. 135 pp.

[7] U. S. Bureau of the Census, *Mobility of the Population of the United States, March 1963 to March 1964, Population Characteristics,* Series (P-20), No. 141, Washington, 1965. 50 pp.

mobility rates of around 20 for male wage and salary workers in white collar, manual, and service jobs. Also the migration rate (based on workers who lived in a different county from that lived in a year earlier) was higher for hired farm workers than for other major civilian occupational categories.

Mobility Rates of Male Wage and Salary Workers, March 1963–March 1964, in Percentages

(Persons 14 years old and over)

			Intercounty Movers (Migrants)				
					Between States		
Wage and Salary Workers	*All Movers*	*Within-County Movers*	*Total*	*Within a State*	*Total*	*Contig-uous*	*Non-contig-uous*
Total	20.9	14.1	6.8	3.5	3.3	1.2	2.1
White collar	20.0	11.8	8.1	4.1	4.1	1.6	2.5
Manual	21.3	15.5	5.8	3.1	2.7	0.9	1.7
Service	20.0	14.4	5.6	3.0	2.7	0.7	1.9
Farm	29.2	18.5	10.7	5.2	5.5	2.0	3.5

Source: U.S. Bureau of the Census, Series P-20, No. 141, *Mobility of the Population of the United States, March 1963 to March 1964.*

Higher rates of mobility and migration stem, to a large extent, from characteristics of the hired farm worker occupation. Among these are: (1) seasonality of employment with associated nonfarm-to-farm and farm-to-farm moves. About 65 percent of the hired farm work force lived in nonfarm places in December, a month of low farm work activity. Yet many of these workers have moved from a nonfarm place to a farm for a period of employment and have returned to a nonfarm place, but not necessarily to the same house or even the same city or town. (2) A high proportion (about 40 percent) of the workers have more than one employer in the year, involving farm-to-farm moves in many cases. (3) Probably most important, however, is the significant proportion of workers who travel about the country (11 percent) while engaging in and looking for farm work. Another factor that might be mentioned is the high proportion (about 55 percent) of workers who live in rented or rent-free houses, from which moves can be made with relative ease.

About 11 percent of the wage and salary farm workers made an intercountry move between 1963 and 1964, and nearly equal proportions of these workers (about 5.5 percent) moved within a state and between states. Of those moving state to state a slightly higher proportion ended up in a noncontiguous state rather than a state contiguous to their native state.

A great deal of the attention given to hired farm workers is focused on the migratory group which travels about the country while seeking and engaging in hired farm work. Migration in search of work often aggravates problems of low income, unemployment, and underemployment, and presents a multitude of other social and economic problems for workers, and their family members, particularly to women and young children. Being highly visible and often acute, problems of these workers are brought to the attention of the public to a greater extent than are those of other farm workers.

The mobility "streams," and thus the periodic geographic movement, of migratory workers are much better known than the patterns of more permanent mobility of hired farm workers. A schematic chart developed by the Department of Labor shows the origin and generalized travel patterns of seasonal migratory farm workers (Figure 4). Originating in Texas and Florida, two distinctive groups fan out through the Central and Western States and along the Atlantic Coast and other Eastern States. Other smaller groups from Arizona and New Mexico travel to and work in California, Washington, and Oregon.

Certain states regulate labor camps, conditions of travel, day care for children, working hours of children under 16, the activities of farm labor contractors and crew leaders, and other conditions of work of migratory farm laborers. Federal legislation requires that crew leaders register with the Employment Service and regulates their activities. The Economic Opportunity Act has special provisions for programs to improve housing, sanitation, and day care of migratory children. The Migrant Health Act provides for special programs designed to improve the health conditions and medical facilities available to migratory workers and their family members. Although these projects include new and imaginative features, in total they are not likely to go far in solving the special problems of the entire group of

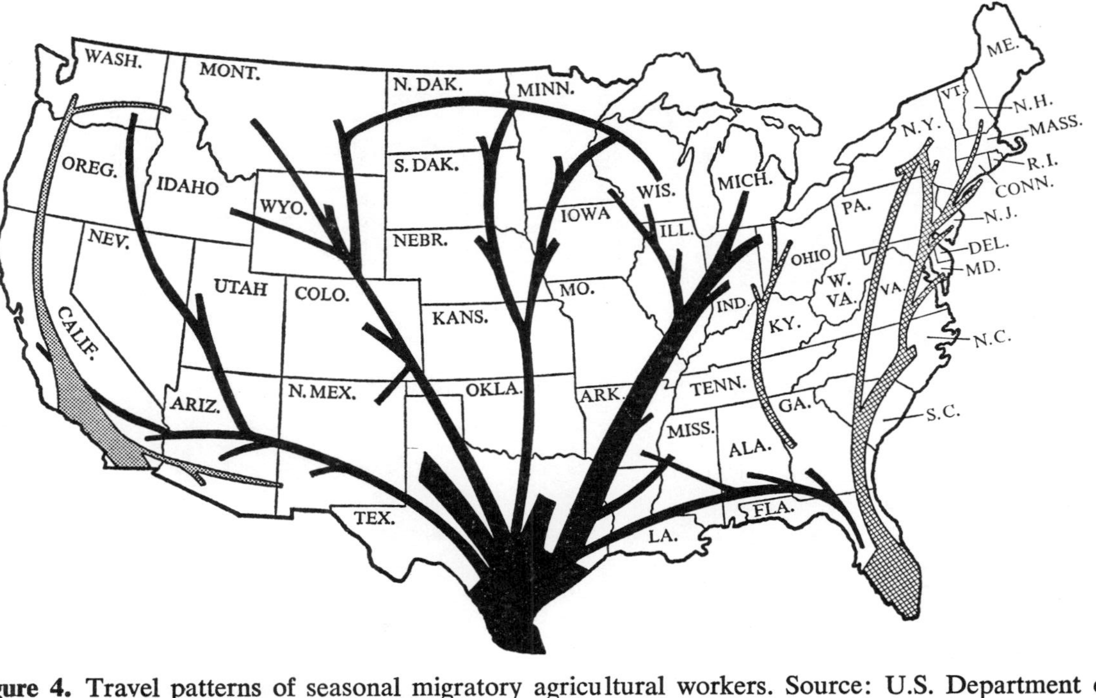

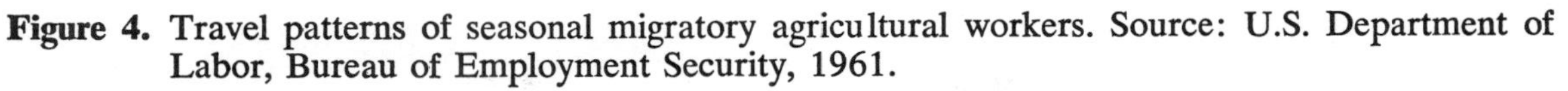

Figure 4. Travel patterns of seasonal migratory agricultural workers. Source: U.S. Department of Labor, Bureau of Employment Security, 1961.

domestic workers who travel about the country in connection with their agricultural work. And most of these programs dealing with farm workers do not reach the nonmigratory workers, who comprise about 90 percent of all hired farm workers.

Seasonal Work Patterns of Hired Farm Workers. Seasonality of farm work is recognized as one of the constant problems facing farm wage workers. Annual worker plans, designed to provide maximum employment to workers, must necessarily recognize the incontrovertible fact that many farm operations can provide employment for only part of a year. And as mechanization and other technological developments reduce the overall demand for hired farm labor, in the future as in the past, the proportion of short-time workers will increase, and their periods of employment on farms are likely to be of shorter duration or, at best, no longer than now on the average.

Casual workers did about 80 percent of their farm wage work in 5 months in 1964—June through October. Noncasual workers, on the other hand, did only a little more than half their work in these months. Figure 5 illustrates the 1964 seasonal work patterns of other significant groups of farm wage workers.

As important as information on periods of employment of hired farm workers are data on their periods of unemployment. We have estimated that of the 3.4 million persons who did some hired farm work in 1964, some 700,000 were unemployed at some time during the year. Of these, about 160,000 were unemployed 27 weeks or longer and some 200,000 had three or more periods of unemployment. Unless they have qualified for unemployment insurance benefits through nonagricultural wage work, hired farm workers and their families are without protection during periods of unemployment.

Employment and Earnings of Hired Farm Workers. Low farm-wage rates, coupled with short average duration of farm work, make the annual earnings of farm wage workers low. On the average, their earnings are lower than the earnings of other major occupational groups.

The USDA series indicates that in July 1, 1964, the farm wage rate per hour for workers who did not receive board or room averaged $1.13; a year later the average was $1.17. In two states the July 1965 average was 65 cents an hour; in five it was $1.40 or more. The rate was below $1.00 an hour in thirteen states, where the average was 82 cents an hour. Wage rates are lowest in the South, where about half the workers live and work, or have their home base, as migratory workers do. Rates are somewhat higher in the North Central

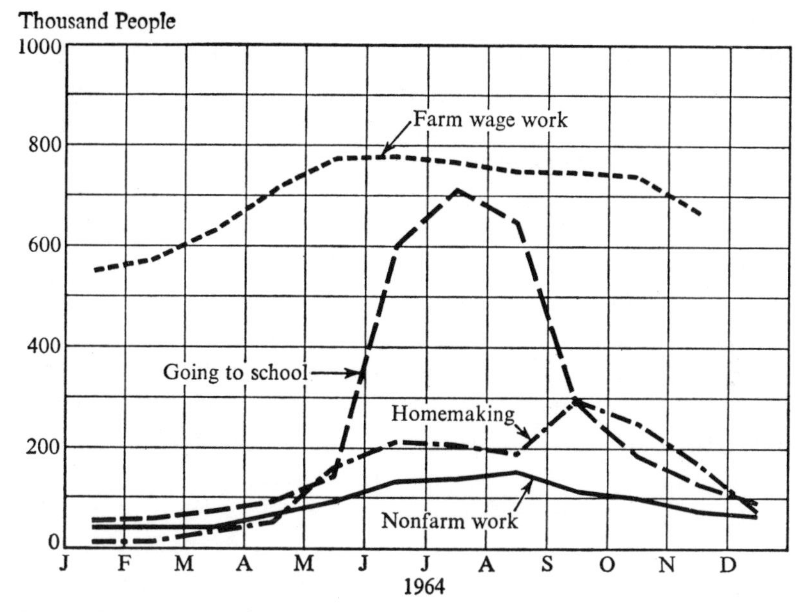

Figure 5. Number of hired farm workers employed in 1964, by their chief activity during the year.

States, which have about one-fifth of the workers, and they are still higher in the Northeastern States. The Western States, which have about 19 percent of the workers, pay the highest wages, on the average.

Although farm wage rates have risen substantially in all parts of the country in recent years, they are still very much lower than rates for most other occupations. In the years since World War II wages in manufacturing industries have more than doubled, while farm wage rates have increased little more than half as much. Production workers in manufacturing industries earned an average of about $2.53 per hour in 1964 [8] compared with $1.17 an hour for farm wage workers.

[8] U. S. Department of Labor, *Bureau of Labor Statistics, Employment and Earnings, Monthly Report on the Labor Force,* and *Special Labor Force Reports,* USDL, BLS, Washington, 1965. Various issues.

Moreover, the relative position of farm workers has actually deteriorated since the end of the War. When adjustments are made for cost of living increases farm workers are shown to be falling behind wage workers in other industries. The relative worsening of the farm-nonfarm wage rate situation holds for all major regions of the country. Even in California, where highest farm wages are paid, on the average, the gap between farm and nonfarm wages has widened in the last 10 years. The ERS annual survey of hired farm workers shows that, as a group, hired farm workers earned about $7.15 a day in cash wages from their farm wage work in 1964. For an average of 80 days of farm work, in 1964 hired farm workers earned $578.

It should be noted that throughout this section of the chapter daily and yearly earnings refer only to the cash wages received by workers and do not include the value of perquisites or fringe benefits furnished without charge by the employer. Actually hired farm workers generally receive less in the way of fringe benefits than do nonagricultural workers. A substantial proportion of farm wage workers do receive some perquisites such as room and board, housing, meals, transportation, and use of garden space. In general, the value of these items does not equal the value of health and medical insurance, paid vacations, and other fringe benefits received by industrial workers, and the quality of housing, sanitary facilities, and other housing equipment provided for farm wage workers is very often substandard.

One of the major features of the hired farm working force is the great variation among major groups in the average number of days of employment and related daily and yearly earnings from farm wage work. A few facts will adequately demonstrate this variation in 1964:

—1.4 million casuals averaged 9 days of work and earned $57.

—2.0 million noncasuals averaged 129 days and earned $933.

On the average, casual workers earned $5.85 a day when they worked on farms.

—Men averaged $6.90 a day and women $5.15.

—Nonmigratory workers averaged $5.80 a day; domestic migratory workers earned $6.75.

—Persons who were heads of households averaged $7.05 a day; other household members earned $5.50.

Even among noncasuals, many are not in the labor force, or they do types of work other than farm wage work most of the year. Since 1947–49 the proportion of noncasuals whose chief activity was farm wage work has been declining and the proportion not in the labor force the greater part of the year has been increasing.

Among the noncasuals:

—1.3 million seasonal workers averaged 64 days of work and earned $400 from farm wage work.

—0.3 million regulars averaged 198 days and earned $1,432.

—0.3 million year-rounds averaged 321 days and earned $2,560.

—Whites averaged 134 days at $8.15 a day, earning $1,094 in cash wages.

—Nonwhites averaged 119 days at $5.10 a day, earning $609.

—Workers in the West received the highest daily wages, $11.15; those in the South received the lowest, $5.75.

—Nonmigratory workers averaged 131 days at $6.95 a day, earning $910.

—Domestic migratory workers averaged 120 days at $9.00 a day, earning $1,083.

About 2.1 million persons did farm wage work only (FWO workers), and about 1.3 million were employed at both farm and nonfarm wage work (FNF workers) in 1964.

—FWO workers had about 100 days of farm wage employment and earned $698.

—FNF workers did an average of 98 days of nonfarm wage work and 49 days of farm wage work and earned total wages of $1,379.

—FWO workers earned about $6.95 a day from farm wage work; FNF workers averaged about $7.70 a day.

—FNF workers earned about $10.10 a day from their nonfarm wage work.

CHARACTERISTICS OF THE POPULATION OF HIRED FARM-WORKER HOUSEHOLDS

Although systematic data have been available for many years on hired farm workers, little has been known about the population of all ages associated with these workers. Yet such data are pertinent in a number of contexts. By almost any measure, the occupation of farm-wage worker ranks as poorest in income and education of worker, housing, continuity of employment, and extent of inclusion in the conventional social protections of unemployment compensation, disability insurance, minimum wage or collective bargaining laws. Thus it is relevant to have information not only on the farm workers themselves but also on size and characteristics of the population dependent in some degree on them.

In this second part of the chapter, farm-worker households are those households which had at least one member who had engaged in hired farm work in 1962. The population of these households was cross-classified by characteristics of the household head and by the amount of hired farm work done by members of the household. The result is analogous to occasional past studies that have dealt with the population of farm-operator households.

In December 1962 there were 2.6 million households in the United States with one or more of the 3.6 million persons who did farm work for wages or salary in 1962. The total population of these households was 11.2 million persons, or 6.1 percent of the total United States population. This represents the maximum number of persons in the nation who had some direct degree of dependence on hired farm work for their support.

Of the population in farm-worker households, 3,054,000 persons, or 27 percent, were nonwhite. Thus nonwhites, who made up about 12 percent of the general population in 1962, were greatly overrepresented in the farm wage-worker population.[9] Most of the nonwhites are Negroes, but Japanese, Filipinos, and American Indians are also included.

One-half the population of farm wage-worker households were children and youth under 18 years of age. This figure compares with about 37 percent for all households in the United States. Households

[9] Information on the general population used for comparative purposes in this report is from various publications of the U. S. Bureau of the Census. Specifically, U. S. Bureau of the Census, *U. S. Census of Population: 1960. General Social and Economic Characteristics,* United States summary. *Final Report* PC (1)-1C. U. S. Government Printing Office, Washington, 1962, 344 pp.

with one or more farm wage workers were somewhat larger (4.4 persons) than the average household in the United States (3.8). Nonwhite farm-worker households averaged 4.9 persons in 1962 compared with 4.2 persons in white households, a difference due mainly to the larger average number of children and youth in the nonwhite households. At the time of the survey, nonwhite households averaged 2.8 persons under age 18, whereas white households averaged 2.0 children and youth. Nonwhite households also typically contained a larger number of persons who had done farm-wage work in 1962 (1.7) than did white households (1.3).

Sex and Age Distribution of Household Heads. Farm wage-worker households have males as the head somewhat more often than do other households. In 1962, 87 percent of farm-worker households had a male as the head compared with 82 percent of all households. Households with a woman as the head are rather frequent among nonwhite farm workers. More than one-fourth of these nonwhite households do not have a male head as compared with one-twelfth of the white-worker households without a man as the head. The heads of households having farm-wage workers are somewhat younger, on the average, than are the heads of other households. Nearly 50 percent of them, in 1962, were under 45 years of age, compared with 45 percent in the general population. Nonwhite heads were a little older, on the average, than white heads of farm-worker households.

Education of Household Heads. The median years of school completed by heads of households (25 years of age and over) which had one or more persons doing farm-wage work in 1962 was 7.7 years. About 65 percent of these household heads had not gone beyond 8 grades of school. Among nonwhite heads, more than 80 percent had not gone beyond 8 grades in school. Of the family heads in the general population in 1962, on the other hand, only 35 percent had not gone beyond 8 grades of school. For nonwhite heads, in the general population, the percentage was 56.

Total Family Income in 1962. Households in which one or more members had done some farm wage work had a median net money income from all sources of about $2,600 in 1962. The median for white households of $3,156 was more than double that of $1,505 for nonwhite households. Part of the difference in total income resulted from the fact that a higher proportion of nonwhite households were headed by persons who for the greater part of the year were not in the labor force or were unemployed. Also, more white than nonwhite heads were engaged primarily in nonfarm work rather than in farm wage work.

Migratory Status. There were 178,000 households, containing 604,-000 persons of all ages, in which the head did some migratory farm work in 1962. These households do not include all the 380,000 people who did migratory farm work during the year. Some migratory workers either did not come from households where the head was a migratory worker or lived in group quarters which were not defined as households. It is estimated that about 300,000 households had one or more migratory workers. The relatively small population in households headed by migratory farm workers (5.4 percent of the total farm-worker household population) is a reminder that the migratory-worker population is a very small segment of the total group with some dependence on hired farm work.

DEPENDENCE ON HIRED FARM WORK

The degree of dependence of families on hired farm work for their livelihood varies greatly. For some, farm wage work is the principal source of income; for others, it supplements income from nonfarm work or from farming.

Population with Minor Dependence on Hired Farm Work. Of the 11.2 million people living in all farm-worker households, 6.4 million, or more than half, were in households in which the head of the house did less than 25 days of hired farm work. The other household members had a combined total of less than 150 days of such work. About 90 percent of them earned less than $100 from hired farm work, and the group averaged over $3,000 of income per family from other sources. These households clearly had only *minor dependence on farm wage work* for their support. It is estimated that less than 5 percent of the net income of the population in this group came from hired farm work.

Compared with other hired-worker households those with minor dependence:

—were least likely to live on a farm. Only 31.5 percent are on farms compared with 41.5 percent of the other farm-worker population;

—were more likely to be from households where a good level of education prevails. More than 25 percent of the household heads had completed high school compared with 15 percent for heads in all other farm-worker households;

—had fewer nonwhites. About one-fourth of the population in these households was nonwhite, a somewhat lower proportion than in other dependence groups;

—had more children 6 to 18 years of age (37 percent against 30 percent in households with moderate or primary dependence).

In other words, many of the casual farm workers come from nonfarm homes with good educational levels, and a high proportion are school-age children earning money on local farms after school hours or in periods of peak labor need. In 80 percent of the households, only one person did any farm work. The average level of family income in these households of $3,187 was equal to the average of the general farm resident population, and was noticeably higher than that of families with moderate dependence ($1,856) or primary dependence ($2,476).

Population with Moderate Dependence on Hired Farm Work. A second group of households had *moderate dependence on farm wage work.* These were households in which the head performed 25 to 149 days of farm wage work per year (usually less than 75 days) or in which the head did little or no farm work but other members of the household did an aggregate of 150 or more days. The total population in the households of moderate farm work dependence numbered 2.7 million. As a group, such households earned approximately 28 percent of their income from hired farm work.

The population with a moderate dependence on farm wage work consisted of two different types of households. The more numerous were those in which the household head did some farm wage work, but less than 150 days per year. The second type consisted of households where the head did less than 25 days of such work, if any, but the work of one (or more) other household members added up to 150 days or more of hired farm work.

In the households where the head did a substantial amount of farm wage work, there were about 1.9 million people. In these households:

—three-fifths were in the South, a heavier Southern concentration than is true of any other dependence category (except where the head did 150–249 days);

—about three-eighths of the population were nonwhite;

—three-tenths of the people lived in urban areas, a higher proportion than of any other category;

—heads of households also did much nonfarm work and some of them were farm operators;

—others were adults who were not usually in the labor force. Also included were many people who wanted but could not obtain more work;

—17 percent of the heads who had performed 25–149 days of farm wage work in 1962 were unemployed in December of that year.

This was the poorest group of farm-worker households, with an average total family income of $1,571 and only $418 a year from farm wage work. To some extent low income results from the fact that a higher proportion of household heads in this group was nonwhite and a higher proportion was of late middle age or older (and in a state of semiretirement) than is true among regular workers.

The second group of households in the moderate dependence class is much smaller, including about 748,000 persons. In these households in which 150 days or more of farm wage work were performed by household members, but little or none by the head, two types of situations prevail; those in which the household head was a farm operator (29 percent) and his children or wife worked for wages for him or some other farmer, and those in which the head was too old to work (21 percent were 65 years of age and over).

—Only a little over a fourth of the population was nonwhite.

—23 percent lived in urban places.

—There was very little unemployment among heads of these households (only 1.6 percent of those in the labor force).

—Over 40 percent were engaged primarily in nonfarm work at the time of the survey.

The average level of family income ($3,218) was better than in the homes of full-time farm wage workers, despite the high proportion of elderly heads. Only a fourth of the households in this group had less than $2,000 income from all sources compared with five-eighths of the households in the other group with moderate dependence on farm wage work (where the household head works for 25–149 days).

Population with Primary Dependence on Hired Farm Work. These are households in which the head did at least 150 days per year of hired farm work. They contained a population of 2.2 million persons in 1962 and averaged receiving about 82 percent of their income from farm wage work. Workers in these households performed about 64 percent of all days of hired farm work that were done in the nation although they contained only 20 percent of the farm-worker household population.

In about two-thirds of the households with a primary dependence on farm wage work the head was the only person who did such work. Such households actually averaged a larger total income than those in which wives or children engaged in farm work also. Not all the heads of these households, however, had full-time farm work. A full work year is about 250 days (on a 5-day basis), but a third of the heads in the primary dependence group had only 150 to 249 days of farm work yearly. The low-average family income of this latter group suggests that employment of other family members is relatively limited and that there is a good deal of underemployment among the heads of these households.

In the households with primary dependence on hired farm work:

—about one-fourth was nonwhite;

—probably because of their rather constant connection with agriculture, nearly half the people lived on farms, and most of the others lived in rural-nonfarm homes;

—among the four major regions of the nation, a larger number of households with primary dependence on farm wage work were located in the South than in any other single region, as is true of all classes of farm workers;

—in the Northeast and the West the relative number of households with primary dependence was disproportionately large—24 percent in each region. In the South 20 percent and in the North Central States 16 percent of the households were primarily dependent on farm wage work.

INCIDENCE OF LOW LEVELS OF INCOME AND EDUCATION AMONG HIRED FARM-WORKER HOUSEHOLDS

As noted in the 1964 Economic Report of the President, households with heads who were farm laborers or foreman have a very high incidence of poverty (defined as households with less than $3,000 income in a year). In 1962, 56 percent of the households headed by farm laborers and foremen had less than $3,000 family income, an incidence of low income exceeded only by households headed by domestic service workers.

Among farm-worker households in 1962, the same proportion (56 percent) had total income of less than $3,000. The incidence of low income was particularly high among nonwhites (83 percent), most of whom are in the South, and among households headed by persons who had done some migratory farm wage work in 1962 (71 percent).

Among the three farm-work dependency classes incidence of low annual income was highest among families that did some hired farm work but did not have regular or full employment in either farm or nonfarm work or a combination thereof, in other words, in the moderate-dependence category.

Dependency Class	*Proportion of Farm-Worker Households with Less than $3,000 Family Income in 1962 (percentage)*
Total	56
Minor	48
Moderate	71
Primary	61

The relationship of income and education has received much attention in recent years. Low levels of education of many hired farm workers mean that they can obtain only relatively low-paying types of farm and nonfarm jobs. Among households with persons who had done some hired farm work in 1962 that were headed by persons at least 25 years old, 65 percent of the household heads had completed only 8 grades of school or less, about one-third of whom had completed less than 5 grades of school. Households where the head had completed less than 5 years of schooling averaged about $2,000 income from all sources and those where the head had 5 to 8 years averaged about $3,000 total family income. Higher average levels of income were associated with each higher level of educational attainment of the head, with those headed by persons who had completed high school averaging nearly $5,800.

Within each educational category, the average income of nonwhite households was less than that of white households. In fact, the average income of households headed by nonwhites who had completed high school was only a few hundred dollars higher than the income of white families with a head who had completed less than 5 years of school.

Households headed by migratory workers averaged about $2,600 from all sources in 1962. Among these households the same relationships, pointed out above, existed between level of education and family income. Households headed by persons with less than 5 years of school completed averaged about $1,900 family income whereas those with heads who had completed high school had an average family income of $4,200.

Among households in the three categories of dependency on farm wage work, the relationships between income and education of the household head followed the general pattern. Households with moderate dependence on farm wage work headed by persons who had completed less than 5 years of school averaged only $1,600 income; households with minor dependence on such work, headed by persons who had completed at least high school averaged about $6,200 family income in 1962.

In farm-worker households, fully one-half the population consisted of children under 18 years of age, and nearly two-thirds of the children and youth under 18 years in households in some way dependent on farm wage work were in households where the head had completed 8 grades of school or less. In the primary and moderate dependence categories over 70 percent of the children were in households headed by persons who had had no high school education.

About three-eighths of the children in households having a primary dependence on farm wage work are in homes where the head of the house has less than 5 years of schooling. These homes average 3 children under 18 years each, compared with an average of 2 children in the other primary-dependence homes of higher education. Thus, within the farm worker population, children are overrepresented in households of extremely low education.

About 3 million, or 54 percent, of the children and youth were in households in which total family income in 1962 was less than $3,000. These 3 million young people comprise 27 percent of the 11.4 million children and youth under 18 years of age living in all households in the United States where family income totaled less than $3,000 in 1962.

It is the heavy proportion of children in farm-worker households that in part creates concern over the welfare of this population. The low education of the majority of the parents and the intermittent and seasonal nature of the work of many of them produce conditions which help to perpetuate low education and low aspirations from one generation to another.

[3]

Farm Labor Adjustments to Changing Technology

G. S. TOLLEY AND B. M. FARMER

According to estimates by Loomis and Barton, man-hour inputs in United States agriculture are projected to decline 48 percent from 1960 to 1980.[1] Basing their work on an analysis of Heady and Tweeten, Heady and Ball [2] estimated that hired labor will decline 30 to 35 percent between 1960 and 1980 whereas family labor will decline 45 to 55 percent. Daly [3] projected a decline in the number of farms from 3.7 million in 1962–63 to 2.0 million in 1980. Daly believes that hours per farm of operator and family workers will not change much, but hours per farm of hired work he projects to increase, so that the decline in the hours worked by hired farm workers is less than a third. Most projections of the changing number of farms indicate declines in the future at about the same rate as in the 1950s, when there was a 30 percent decline in the number of farms. Seymour Smidt and Tolley [4] projected labor inputs for 1980 under a variety of assumptions about underlying conditions leading to changes in agriculture. The projected decline in labor inputs under the alternative assumptions was from a farm labor force figure on 5.7 million in 1960 to a range of 3.0 to 5.3 million in 1980.

G. S. TOLLEY is a Professor in the Department of Economics in North Carolina State University (on leave with USDA). B. M. Farmer is a former graduate assistant in the Department of Economics of the same University.

[1] USDA Technical Bulletin 1238, 1961. U. S. Statistical Bulletin 233, revised 1961.

[2] E. O. Heady and A. G. Ball, "Economic Growth of the Farm Firm and Projected Changes in Farming," *Structural Changes in Commercial Agriculture*, CAED Report 24, Iowa State University, 1965.

[3] Rex Daly, *Agriculture in the Years Ahead*, USDA, 1964.

[4] S. Smidt and G. S. Tolley, "Agriculture and the Secular Position of the U. S. Economy," *Econometrica*, 1964.

In short, every look that is taken ahead shows a continuation of the general nature of adjustments that have been going on in the last few years of substantial declines in labor inputs. The range of uncertainty about actual labor inputs comes partly from demand uncertainty but more importantly from uncertainty about labor input required to satisfy this demand, that is, labor productivity. There may be only moderate labor declines, or there may be more substantial declines, but almost certainly there will be a continued general decline in labor input for both hired and family workers.

Let us now take a less aggregative look. An overview of the structure of labor use in agriculture is given in Tables 1 through 4. Comparisons within any one table are instructive, but the reader is cautioned against relying on conclusions reached from a comparison of the four tables. Differences in definitions, as for instance between total man-hours and average annual employment, and several other complications make the tables noncomparable. Table 1 shows what has been happening over the last few decades to total man-hours of farm labor and how the total has been distributed among individual crop and livestock products. The conditions of employment and the adjustment problems are markedly different for full-time hired workers, seasonal hired workers, farm operators (who are considered self-employed), and farm family workers who are unpaid. Table 2 gives an indication of how average annual employment is distributed among these types of persons and reveals that all contribute substantially to farm-labor input. The self-employed, supplying about half the total, are the largest of the four contributing groups. As revealed in Table 3, seasonal hired work is heavily concentrated among relatively few crops. Cotton, vegetables, and fruits are the most important groups and utilize somewhere near equal amounts of seasonal labor. By activity, as given in Table 4, well over half the seasonal hired labor is for harvesting.

Let us now try to relate future labor use to specific technologies and thereby obtain ideas as to adjustment implications of the technologies and policy problems implied. Berkwood Farmer in a study at North Carolina State University has been attempting to see what specific technologies on the horizon and factors affecting rate of adoption may mean for future labor use. Survey schedules were obtained throughout the country during the summer of 1964 in order

Table 1 Man-hours of Labor Used for Farmwork, by Groups of Enterprises, United States, Selected Periods and Years, 1910–1964 [a]

(In millions of hours)

	1910–1914	*1939*	*1950*	*1964*
All farm work [b]	23,127	20,675	15,137	8,420
Livestock and livestock products [c]				
All	4,836	5,998	5,548	3,282
Meat animals	1,151	1,301	1,451	1,254
Milk cows	2,658	3,452	2,749	1,393
Poultry	786	993	1,161	465
Crops [d]				
All	12,963	10,581	6,922	3,963
Feed grains	3,915	2,745	1,484	513
Hay and forage	1,263	1,173	695	464
Food grains	905	528	327	177
Vegetables	668	802	643	385
Fruits and nuts	800	760	619	571
Sugar crops	197	203	135	91
Cotton	3,937	2,390	1,298	586
Tobacco	457	871	745	545
Oil crops	78	226	199	191

[a] Data found in 1965 issue of *Changes in Farm Production and Efficiency: A Summary Report,* U.S. Department of Agriculture Statistical Bulletin 233, Washington, D.C., revised July 1965.

[b] Includes labor used on crops, livestock, and overhead.

[c] For livestock included in each group, see Table 1, footnotes 3 to 7, of publication named in footnote a, above.

[d] For crops included in each group see *Ibid.,* Table 1, footnotes 8 to 16.

Note: Supplement III to the publication quoted contains a table similar to this one for each region.

Table 2 Average Annual Employment in Agriculture by Type of Worker

	1964	1963	1962	1961
	(000)	(000)	(000)	(000)
Employment in agriculture	4,761	4,946	5,190	5,463
Wage and salary	1,582	1,676	1,666	1,733
(Seasonal hired farm workers)	(705)	(675)	(707)	(749)
Self-employed	2,366	2,437	2,619	2,744
Unpaid family	813	834	905	985

Source: Current Population Survey and Bureau of Employment Security.

Table 3 Estimated Average Annual Employment of Seasonal Hired Labor, by Crop, 1964 [a]

Crops	*Number (thousands)*	*Percent*
All crops	705.2	100.0
Cotton	129.3	18.3
All vegetables	154.6	21.9
Tomatoes	28.8	4.1
Beans	19.8	2.8
Potatoes	18.6	2.6
Other vegetables	87.4	12.4
All fruits	131.5	18.6
Citrus	26.4	3.7
Strawberries	25.2	3.6
Grapes	14.2	2.0
Other fruits	65.7	9.3
Hay and grain	52.7	7.5
Hay	21.0	3.0
Grain	31.6	4.5
Tobacco	63.4	9.0
Livestock	19.8	2.8
Other crops	153.9	21.8

[a] Includes employment in harvesting, cultivation, and other activities.
Source: Bureau of Employment Security, In-Season Farm Labor Reports.

to ascertain detailed cultural practices currently being used and the labor inputs required for each cultural practice. The criteria for selection of areas were, first, that there should be production of commodities which are major labor users and, second, that these should have present or potential policy problems. Production of dairy cattle, hogs, cotton, wheat, and feed grains in various parts of the country was sampled. The survey results give an indication of what proportion of production is currently under various kinds of technology and what the man-hours required for each technology are. The differences in practices being used by farmers, even in the same region, are striking.

A companion part of this study is aimed at estimating potential labor inputs. Information pertaining to new technologies was ob-

Table 4 Estimated Average Annual Employment of Seasonal Hired Agricultural Workers by Crop Activity, 1964 [a]

Crop Activity	*Number* [b] *(thousands)*	*Percent of Total*
All Activities	705.4	100.0
General	78.7	11.2
Cultivating	137.4	19.5
Cotton	46.7	6.6
Fruits	32.7	13.9
Other crops	57.9	8.3
Harvesting	415.6	58.9
Cotton	73.2	10.4
Vegetables	132.0	18.7
Beans	18.8	2.7
Tomatoes	26.4	3.7
Potatoes	15.8	2.2
Other vegetables	71.1	10.1
Other crops	78.3	11.1
Activity unspecified	73.6	10.4

[a] From Farm Labor Developments, U.S. Department of Labor, January 1965.

[b] Average of 15th of month employment.

tained from physical scientists at various land-grant colleges, and from USDA personnel in Washington, D.C., and Beltsville, Maryland. For each major crop, questions such as the following were asked:

1. What new technologies are available and will become available within the next 10 years in the production of a given commodity?
2. What is the likelihood of their adoption?
3. If adopted, what effects will there be on future farm size, output, and man-hours?
4. What type of management will be required for the adoption of the new technology?

Based on the answers, estimates were made of the savings in labor that would result from bringing present practices up to potentials. Some considerations not taken account of in the potentials could make the estimated labor changes conservative; other considerations could make them optimistic. Not all operators will adopt them even if the technologies are profitable. The profitability of some of the newer practices depends on size of operation, which may be limited by land or capital availability. However, the net effect of any neglected considerations probably is to make the estimated labor changes conservative. All the potential technologies of this study are now physically operational. Research has shown many of them to be profitable. Some were found in the survey to be already in use by some farmers. Within 10 years new technologies not now anticipated may be developed and become available.

Table 5 compares demand projections with the potential improvement in the average labor coefficient if all farmers were to use the best technology known today. A greater decline in the labor coeffi-

Table 5 Potential Demand and Labor Coefficient Changes, 1964 to 1975–80

Commodity	*Percentage Shift in Demand*		*Potential Percentage Change in Labor Coefficient*
	1975	*1980*	
Dairy			
New York	+25	+37	−82
Wisconsin			−75
Cattle			
Iowa	+32	+49	−56
Hog			
Illinois	+30	+47	−54
Cotton			
North and South Carolina Coastal Plain	+21	+32	−91
Texas			−54
Wheat			
Kansas	+17	+25	−23
Feed grains			
Iowa	+16	+24	−50 [a]
Illinois			−41 [b]
Illinois			−37 [c]
Nebraska			−22 [d]
Texas			−28 [e]

[a] Corn on Iowa cattle farms. [b] Illinois cash corn. [c] Corn on Illinois hog farms. [d] Nebraska corn practices. [e] Sorghum on Texas cotton farms.

cient than increase in demand implies that to equate supply and demand it will be necessary for less labor to be used. Thus by glancing down the table we can see where the biggest pressures to eject labor from agriculture are likely to occur. More will be said about the adjustments accompanying this ejection later in this chapter.

The 75 to 80 percent decline in the labor coefficient for dairy practices comes roughly equally from three sources: automated feeding, more highly mechanized milking systems, and increase in milk yields per cow. In accounting for the 56 percent decline in the labor coefficient for cattle, going to fully automative feeding is about three times as important as increased average weights per animal. The decline in labor coefficient in hogs is due about equally to the possibility of developing fully automated feeding and more efficient cleaning practices.

The overwhelmingly important consideration accounting for the large potential declines in labor coefficients for cotton is use of herbicides reducing need for chopping and hoeing labor. The projected potential decrease in labor coefficient for wheat is due about equally to use of larger equipment and to increased yields per acre. These two factors also account for the potential decline of the labor coefficient for feed grains.

The results for cotton are dramatic but largely a continuation of what we have been witnessing for several years. The more serious portent for policy purposes may be the results for dairying. The implication is that even allowing for substantial increases in demand, perhaps a 50 percent reduction in labor will be necessary to equate supply and demand.

Insofar as the reduction in labor input can be achieved through using less hired labor, production control policy problems will be eased. It is when operator labor is squeezed that particularly difficult problems are encountered, as operators attempt to remain in business competing with one another. The full analysis of the implications of these projections for adjustment problems has not yet been completed. The considerations entering into this analysis may be briefly reviewed because they throw light on how the nature of coming adjustment problems is importantly related to potential changes in labor coefficients.

Concern with adjustment requires attention to amounts of man-hours supplied by operator labor, other family labor, and hired labor. It will be assumed that the number of farmers who at the present time have a basic farm production unit large enough to adopt the potential techniques will adopt them within the next few years. Other operators with below optimum production size units will have to wait to consolidate their holdings by taking over production units of retiring operators until their production units are increased to the size where it will be economically feasible for the adoption to occur.

The following assumptions are important in the adjustment process:

1. On farms where operator and/or operator-family labor perform most of the work except in peak seasons, it is assumed that farmers adopting the new technologies will eliminate practically all seasonal hired labor.

2. On farms where operator and year-round hired laborers do all the work, there will be either an enlargement in the overall farming operation and retention of some of the hired laborers or the hired laborers will be released and the size of operations kept about the same.

3. On farms with the operator doing all the work, the adoption of new technologies will allow for farm unit(s) expansion.

Shifts in product supply curves will not be as great as suggested by considering only the actual changes in the labor coefficient. Even in the absence of supply-demand equilibration, the actual change in labor coefficients results partly from a downward shift in labor demand and partly from an increase in output produced by the remaining labor. The downward shifts in demand for labor take the form of less hired labor, less family work, and reduced hours worked by the operator. To estimate the actual change in supply of farm products accompanying the actual change in the labor coefficient in the absence of feedback, we need to separate the two effects on the labor coefficient.

On one hand, if adjustment to new technologies took the form completely of shifts in farm labor demand, they would lead to no increase in the supply of farm products. On the other hand, if there were no downward shifts in labor demand associated with adoption of the new technologies, there would be an increase in supply exactly inversely proportional to the change in the labor coefficients. Reality may vary between these two extremes. The next step, then, is to separate the downward labor demand shifts from upward commodity supply shifts accompanying changes in labor coefficients, in order to compare commodity supply with future commodity demand.

The difference between prospective supply and demand is impetus to feedback leading to product or factor market equilibrations that will make future amount supplied equal to future amount demanded. In the absence of government programs, product prices would change in response to supply-demand divergences. This would affect supply through interrelated changes in farm resources devoted to particular enterprises, change in the number of farms and possible effects on the rate of adoption of technology itself. For instance, a change in product prices may affect the profitability of adopting a new technology. As another example, if number of farms is affected, then availability of factors for expansion will be affected and so may change the adoption of technologies which depend on scale. With government programs, a similar set of interrelated equilibrations is to be expected resulting from changes in factor availabilities or marketing quotas accompanying policy attempts to keep amounts produced approximately equal to amounts demanded.

The analysis above underscores the fact that there are many different manpower-related problems in agriculture, the major ones having their roots in technological change. How these impinge depend on the managerial and employment status of workers and on the skill selectivity of technological changes. The basic similarities between the manpower problems associated with agriculture and those of the rest of the nation have not been adequately recognized. They are of one piece. As in the rest of the economy, rapid technological changes of the last few decades have been displacing unskilled workers and persons of lower managerial ability. Furthermore, the adjustment processes and problems have been similar in that hired labor has been directly displaced whereas persons in entrepreneurial positions have been able to hang on, barely making a living, long after it is clear that there is no place for them in the new technologies, for which they have neither the managerial aptitudes nor the hope of acquiring the necessary resources. Thus the proprietor of the corner grocery store, the family fisherman, and the operator of the small farm all find themselves in similar circumstances.

Two manpower policy problems of particular current importance may be considered. One is related to hired workers, the other to self-employed farm operators. Both are policy problems associated with human resource adjustment to scientific advances in production methods.

First, consider the impacts of minimum wage legislation for hired farm labor. We do not have precise estimates of these impacts, but we do have some definite views about the need for obtaining estimates. Too often the impacts are treated as a closed issue. On the one hand, some consider it obvious that the only important effects of a minimum wage will be to throw persons out of work and to result in lower wages of those not covered. On the other hand, there are those who consider only the increased incomes of covered workers.

A question to be researched is: How many workers will be displaced from industries covered by a minimum wage? To answer this question requires recognizing the competition of the hired workers. In farming, hired-worker production in one region is competing with that of hired workers in other regions and with that of family farm workers. It is well known that hired farm wage rates vary markedly among regions and are lowest in the South. This fact gives clues as to where the major impact of a minimum wage would be and provides a starting point for analyzing the impacts in more detail. The eliminatability of hired farm labor from the production process depends on the substitutability of other inputs for labor. A "smooth production function" assumption is likely to be misleading. It may be better to think, first, of readily available measures that can be taken to eliminate labor, such as the use of herbicides to replace preharvesting cotton labor. Below a given wage level, a cotton grower will not find it profitable to use herbicides; whereas if wages are raised above a certain critical level, he may have an incentive to eliminate virtually all the labor used in controlling weeds. Second, there are ways of eliminating labor that are developable in response to pronounced increases in incentives to reduce the wage bill. Research and promotion of various mechanical means of carrying out crop activities are examples.

The next question is: What happens to any workers who are displaced because of a minimum wage? This unanswered question in fact depends on whether workers find alternative employment and, if so, in what kind of job. If hired farm workers are geographically or occupationally immobile, as many of them are, then in the absence of a minimum wage they may be in low productivity jobs with earnings below what they could earn in alternative employment. Introduction of a minimum wage could induce them to move to jobs where their income is higher and where their contribution to the production of the nation is higher. We believe that empirical investigation related to the mobility of labor will be required to ascertain what the full effects of minimum wages are.

A researchable question requiring the cooperation of sociologists and economists is particularly applicable to migratory farm workers: What are the social costs of the hired farm worker's way of life? An answer to this question would give clues as to how much it is worth to foster research that will eliminate labor, particularly seasonal labor, from agricultural production processes.

Finally, consider a manpower problem related to family farm operators which is less well understood than are hired farm labor problems. This has to do with the so-called boxed-in farm operators. These are farmers on small units who have established themselves in a way of life which has become technologically outmoded. Research based on census information and farm management analysis leaves little doubt that there are at least a million such farmers. Possibly the number is as high as 2 million—which amounts to the great majority of farmers. Many of these are retiring each year, but many are also being added each year because of the continued march of technological potentials. Boxed-in farmers have relatively low earnings and are beyond the age where migration normally occurs. There is more and more recognition that it is quite unrealistic to expect these persons to make substantial geographical or occupational adjustments.

What policy alternatives are to be considered for these farmers who are producing little of value to themselves or to the country? The solution will almost certainly have to be one that is largely "in place." Doing nothing implies a continuation of waste of human resources. Dole payments could better the lot of these families in material terms but would do little for their self-respect or for the nation at large. A view gaining increasing acceptance is that more intense efforts should be made to provide productive employment in private and public activities within commuting distance of rural homes. Aside from traditional kinds of public works, this work could include highway and park beautification and subprofessional employment, particularly in health occupations.

[4]

National Employment, Skills, and Earnings of Farm Labor

THEODORE W. SCHULTZ

The nation's farm labor takes on relevance as a problem. By way of preface, what is the problem and what are the reasons for our concern? The earnings of farm labor per person, hired and self-employed, are in fact very low compared to those of nonfarm labor. But why are they so low?

Is the central problem an inefficient labor market as it serves the farm labor force? If true, presumably the low earnings of farm labor could be raised by some appreciable amount by developing a more efficient labor market. I doubt, however, that this is the key problem when allowance is made for the periodic slackness in the aggregate demand for labor in the United States economy, for the cost of acquiring information about job opportunities, and for the damage that has been done to skills by the long-standing discrimination in the schooling and training of persons in the farm labor force.

Is the problem predominantly that of gains in agricultural productivity? Here presumably the low earnings of farm labor are revealed in "structural maladjustments" that are caused by these gains in agricultural productivity, along with the further presumption that it is beyond the capacity of a normal labor market to correct such "structural maladjustments." This aspect of the dynamics of our economic growth is the source of some of the difficulty that we face here, but it is not, in my judgment, the key problem.

Turning now to still another question: Is the central problem caused by slackness in the aggregate demand for labor? An affirma-

---

THEODORE W. SCHULTZ is Charles M. Hutchinson Distinguished Service Professor of Economics at the University of Chicago.

tive answer would rest on the proposition that the earnings of the farm labor force are reduced more than are the earnings of the nonfarm labor force by such slack in the aggregate demand for labor. In tracing the effects of periodic movement in unemployment on the earnings of farm labor, I would rate this as the first half of the central problem. In this context, I look upon the age and skills (that is, schooling, experience, and training) of the farm labor force, for all practical purposes, as given in the short run. Last, then: Are the capabilities of the farm labor force the second half of the central problem? Without belaboring the economic logic and the relevant attributes of farm labor, let me at this point simply assert the proposition that the primary reason the earnings of the farm labor force are so low is to be found in the lack of skills that the economy demands and that this lack would keep these earnings relatively low, even though the economy were fully employed.

There are other issues, some of which overlap or are integral parts of the four preceding problems. Is there all too little mobility for an efficient functioning of this part of the labor market? Hathaway and Perkins [1] show that there is much more shuttling of labor between the farm and nonfarm sectors than any of us had realized, but the net out movement is thwarted by unemployment and by a lack of marketable skills. The range of occupations is narrow, especially for farm laborers seeking employment consisting mainly of the jobs that are least desirable in pay and in prospects for advancement in the smaller cities. There is a closely related question, namely: Is the response of farm labor to job opportunities in the nonfarm sector slow, sluggish, and thus subject to long lags? The inference to be drawn from the work of Hathaway and Perkins is in general otherwise. The difficulty, so it would appear, is not in preferences that inhibit the response of farm labor or in not trying to satisfy these preferences, but predominantly in the paucity of job opportunities for the low skills that in general characterize farm workers seeking nonfarm employment.

Could it be that farm wages are at fault? They should be higher if

[1] Brian Perkins and Dale Hathaway, *The Movement of Labor between Farm and Nonfarm Jobs,* Research Bulletin 13, Michigan State University, East Lansing, 1966.

they undervalue the economic productivity of such labor in farming. It could be that farm wages lag over time, relative to the rise in real wages generally, and that particular farmers, that is, those who operate large farms and who employ a large number of farm workers, pay less than the going wage and less than the economic productivity of the farm workers they hire. Consider first the rise in wages in manufacturing. We observe that from 1958 to the present manufacturing wages have risen about a fourth, in current dollars, and that over a longer period, say since 1939, hourly farm wages have increased more than fivefold (17 to 93 cents), whereas wages in manufacturing have increased a bit more than fourfold ($0.63 to $2.62.) [2] Consider next who pays the highest wages; we find that, in general, the larger the farm the higher the farm wages. Consider also whether farm wages are sticky and subject to monopolistic determination by farm employers. I know of no firm evidence that would support this characterization of wage determination within agriculture. On the contrary, it is probably one of the more purely competitive parts of the entire labor market. This view is not inconsistent with the fact that the availability of relatively cheap foreign labor for farm work has a measurable depressing effect on farm wages in the areas where such labor is employed. One of the strong implications of this view of farm wages is that legislation to establish minimum wages throughout agriculture is an inappropriate public approach to increase the earnings of the rank and file of *all* farm workers. Although it would benefit some, it would leave others much worse off, and in the process it would increase rather than reduce the poverty among the families of this part of the farm population. But it should also be made clear that for the self-employed part of the farm labor force, that is, farm operators, there are serious obstacles when it comes to leaving their farms in order to take nonfarm jobs.

I take it to be true that no one is so brash as to apply the "guidelines" to farm labor. But should not labor in agriculture receive a special bonus in view of the very large gains in farm output per manhour, which increased 37 percent from 1958 to 1964, whereas farm

[2] The average gross hourly earnings in agriculture were $0.166 in 1939 and $0.929 for July 1965, and those of all manufacturing $0.627 and $2.62 respectively.

wages in current dollars rose only a fourth? Yet a longer view might suggest caution: During the period from 1939 to 1964 this output per manhour in agriculture rose fourfold and the hourly farm wage increased more than fivefold.[3] I shall return to the problem associated with the rapid gains in agricultural productivity.

The implications of this preface are fairly obvious. The central problem is not that the amount of mobility between the farm and nonfarm sectors is unduly small, or that farm wages are sticky and subject to serious imperfections caused by monopoly power exercised by the farmers who employ farm labor and thereby impair the efficient functioning of the labor market. Nor is it predominantly a problem of structural maladjustments arising out of the rapid gains in agricultural productivity which are beyond the reach of the labor market. The problem which should be given highest priority has two fundamental parts, that is, the slack in aggregate demand for labor since 1957, and the low level of marketable skills of the farm labor force generally. The first part of the problem is at this juncture fairly close to being resolved, at least until the rate of unemployment begins to rise once again. The second part is acutely upon us as the unresolved problem that matters most.

I now turn to a consideration of the state of our knowledge and its relevance as we seek solutions to the farm labor problem.

ECONOMIC KNOWLEDGE AND ITS RELEVANCE

Growth and Productivity. We know that our type of economic growth increases the demand for nonfarm products and services much more than for farm products and services. We know also that the type of productivity gains we are experiencing in agriculture reduces the demand for farm labor. Although as history it is still all very recent, we have learned to accept the fact that an advanced economy can increase its agricultural output and at the same time de-

[3] The index of farm output per manhour was 35 in 1939 and 141 in 1964; and gross hourly earnings were $0.166 and $0.904 respectively in *current* dollars, not in terms of real wages.

crease the absolute size of the farm labor force. Nor is this development any longer unique to the United States, with our 60 percent increase in farm output since 1940 along with a reduction by one-half of the farm labor force; a similar development has characterized most of the countries of western Europe since World War II. Has this development spent itself? The answer is no. On the contrary, there are compelling reasons for believing it will continue for a decade and longer; for that matter, as long as we can project the knowledge now available to us. As to relevance, I doubt that there is much point in our trying to make projections of the more distant future changes in "agricultural technology" because of the many unknowns that are concealed from us when it comes to determining the precise sources of the additional production that is loosely attributed to "technological change" and projections also of prospective changes in the prices of products and factors.

Excess Supply of Farm Labor. We know also that the supply of labor in agriculture is excessively large. Studies by Edward Schuh [4] give us some useful estimates of accumulated excess supply after the mid-fifties. The supply would be too large even if we had had full employment since 1957, and if our federal farm programs had not been so biased in favor of income from farm property, and if we had taken steps to reduce the cost to farm people of acquiring information about nonfarm job opportunities because, even so, there would be lags in adjusting to the persistent and rapid shifts in the demands for labor. The exact amount of the excess supply is not of much relevance, for there can be no doubt that it is presently very large. What matters is how to cope with it, how to develop institutions and programs to minimize the excess supply at the least cost possible.

National Employment. We could no doubt forget about national unemployment with impunity if the movements in unemployment were small, ranging between 4 and 5 percent, and if, in addition, our farm labor, hired and self-employed, were all white with a tolerably good high school education, married, with $5,000 of net assets, and none of them were residing in the South and West North Central regions! But

[4] G. Edward Schuh, "The Long-Run Equilibrium in the Hired Farm Labor Force: History and Implications," *Journal of Farm Economics,* Vol. XLIII, December 1961, pp. 1338-39.

to proceed on these two conditional propositions would be the height of irresponsibility.

Hathaway's estimates (Chapter 5 of this book) are very instructive, and it behooves us to use them to the utmost while we await studies on other relevant aspects of national employment. The main inference from his studies supports the large shift in the net additions to the farm labor force associated with the movement in the national rate of unemployment that occurred during the latter half of the fifties. In 1956–57, the third year during which the annual rate of unemployment had been 4.3 percent or slightly less, the net decline in the "beginning farm labor force" was 4.9 percent. The rate of unemployment then jumped to 6.8 percent in 1958, and it was still at 5.5 percent in 1959, and as a consequence the "beginning farm labor force" not only ceased to decline but also reversed itself and rose by 2.1 percent—a shift of 7 percentage points. A rise of 1.2 percentage points in unemployment resulted in a net change of 7 percentage points (adverse) in the "beginning farm labor force."

Beyond this, unfortunately, we are still dependent on general impressions and a few clues derived from economic logic and from data collected for purposes other than to help resolve the problem at hand. I find it difficult to understand why our knowledge of the effects of movements in the rate of national unemployment on farm labor is so inadequate. Why has it suffered so much from neglect in view of the importance of the problem? Why has there been virtually no economic analysis bearing directly on this issue in the Departments of Agriculture and Labor and by agricultural economists in our land-grant colleges of agriculture, allowing for a few exceptions? My answer would be that this gross neglect is the price we have paid for the overemphasis that the USDA has placed on farm commodities and high price supports, and for the overspecialization of land-grant agricultural economists on narrowly conceived production economics of farms. The failure on the part of economists in the Department of Labor in this respect baffles me no end. The belief that minimum wages throughout agriculture are the cure-all for the low earnings of farm labor is a misconception. Nor are training programs likely to be effective, despite their merits in other respects, unless the aggregate demand for labor is maintained at the level we are now approaching.

I feel sure that a slack in the national demand for labor not only reduces the incentives to mobility from our farms but also enlarges the practice of discrimination. My colleague, Harry G. Johnson,[5] points out, and in my judgment correctly, that slack in the labor market reduces measurably the "incentives to change occupation, to educate oneself, or to move geographically" because of the risk of being unemployed afterwards. Also, he writes:

> When jobs are scarce and applicants are plentiful, so jobs have to be rationed, it is inevitable that the rationing will be done according to social standards of deservingness—or more bluntly, by discrimination. Color, sex, age, inexperience, and inferior educational attainment are obvious characteristics that can serve as a means of automatically excluding individuals from the competition for scarce jobs. Moreover, in times of job scarcity those favored by discrimination will be led by collective self-interest to insist on its enforcement, to reduce their own exposure to the risk of unemployment. It is no accident that unemployment falls more heavily on Negroes than on white males, and more heavily on the young than on married men with families.

It is probably true that only Negroes are more vulnerable than farm labor to this rationing of jobs, that is, to such additional job discrimination caused by a slack in the national demand for labor. Farm labor is vulnerable on each of the following counts: few years of schooling, often poor in quality, few skills acquired through nonfarm labor experiences, and a narrow range of poor occupations, which are stagnant or even declining. Since there are also Negroes in the farm labor force, they bear the heaviest burden of all when there is a slack in the national demand for labor.

Economics of Negro Employment in Agriculture. One searches in vain for studies of the job market for Negroes who are in the farm labor force. The demand and supply factors that determine their economic lot are largely concealed in the realm of statistics. An exception is James Maddox's forthcoming study, *Economic Development*

[5] From his paper, "Unemployment and Poverty," *Poverty Amid Affluence.* edited by Leo Fishman, Yale University Press, 1966.

and Manpower Requirements in the South, by the Twentieth Century Fund, for it breaks new ground. A few Negroes are farmers who are quietly abandoning their unproductive farms. But most Negroes who are still identified with agriculture are wage workers, and over two-fifths of these are women. Bowles [6] credits these women with 25 million days of farm work in 1964. Their earnings are pitifully small, $4.00 per day for farm work; but they are the one class of farm workers who nevertheless earn more per day while working on farms than they earn at nonfarm work.[7] Even though no studies have been made of the economics of the jobs held by Negro females in agriculture, no great amount of economic insight is required to predict what would happen to these farm jobs in the event that the present level of minimum wages were applied to them. Nonwhite males account for a fourth of all male farm wage workers, but for them, too, we are ignorant of the underlying demand and supply factors at work. The Negro farm operators who are left are concealed among the 245,000 nonwhite farm operators as of 1960, compared to 603,000 male and 445,000 female nonwhite wage workers as of 1964. Negroes in the South in 1940 accounted for 23 percent, but by 1959 for only 16.5 percent, of all farm operators in that region. The average value of the farms they operated was only one-fourth that of farms with white operators, $6,200 and $25,400 respectively.

What are the underlying economic factors that Negroes in the farm labor force must face? In my judgment they benefited more than any other class of workers from the strong labor market that prevailed from the early forties until 1957, and since then they have been set back more. The number of Negro farm operators, however, declined more rapidly than the number of whites after 1957 because Negro operators find it more difficult than whites to acquire the increasing amount of capital required to farm efficiently, and because our federal farm programs entail particular adverse economic effects that are in general more telling upon Negro than upon white farm operators.

The low skills and the small earnings of Negroes in the farm labor

[6] Gladys K. Bowles, *The Hired Farm Working Force of 1964,* Agricultural Economic Report 82, USDA, Table 5.

[7] *Ibid.,* Table 7.

force are both predominantly a legacy of generations of social and political discrimination.[8] American Negroes have long been suppressed in agriculture. The values and institutions of white people in rural farm communities where there are Negroes are still strong barriers to the social advance and the political representation of Negroes and to their acquiring access to valuable skills on a par with those available to white people. The USDA, also, has a long record of treating Negroes as second class citizens.[9] In sharp contrast, our central cities have been preparing the stage despite all manner of stresses and strains so that Negroes can become first class citizens. Future historians will no doubt discover that Negroes, like Jews, have found in cities protection and opportunity denied to them in the countryside.

Consider for a moment the preferences of Negroes. Given their cultural values which summarize generations of maltreatment as workers in agriculture, what is their job preference? I am convinced that for American Negroes *agriculture is an inferior occupation.* What I mean by "inferior" here can be expressed in economic terms. Suppose Negroes had a real choice, supported by wholly dependable information, between jobs in agriculture and jobs in other sectors which would give them the same level of real earnings. They would prefer the former to the latter. These cultural values are deeply rooted in the history of slavery and in the failure of agricultural institutions since emancipation to grant them social status, human dignity, civil rights, schooling, and economic opportunity.[10] In their desire to get out of agriculture, Negroes have one advantage, namely, most of those in agriculture are young people. As of March 1964, Negroes in

[8] I draw here directly upon my paper, "Urban Developments and Policy Implications for Agriculture," *Investment in Human Capital Series,* Paper 65:08, University of Chicago, September 1, 1965.

[9] U.S. Commission on Civil Rights, *Equal Opportunity in Farm Programs: An Appraisal of Services Rendered by Agencies of the United States Department of Agriculture,* Washington, D. C., 1965. The Secretary of Agriculture, Orville L. Freeman, under date of June 17, 1965, submitted to the President a report of substantial actual progress on the part of the USDA in correcting some of its discriminatory practices.

[10] Closely akin is the low social status of agriculture in many parts of the world. In the Caribbean, for example, agriculture is in general rated very low as an occupation, and this anthropologists attribute predominantly to the cultural legacy of slavery.

the farm population had a median age of 17.6 years, whereas that of whites was 31.9 years.[11]

With respect to the occupational and regional distribution of Negroes, the economy will not approach an economic equilibrium [12] until virtually all Negroes have left agriculture and most of them have migrated and found work outside the Old South, on a par with the migration out of agriculture during recent decades. Paramount in this transformation is a strong, tight national labor market.

INVESTMENT IN FARM PEOPLE

I have noted that lack of valuable skills is a fundamental part of the farm labor problem. The investment approach is an appropriate and efficient way to enhance the earning capacity of farm labor. Here, too, what we know and its relevance require attention, but the promise and importance of this approach lead me to give it a separate heading.

Let me build on full employment as the foundation. Suppose an aggregate demand for labor with little or no slack in the market were maintained for the next five years and longer, the earnings of most persons who are now classified as being in the farm labor force, whether hired or self-employed, would rise relatively, but they would still continue to remain relatively low for the simple reason that the marketable skills of farm people are in general far below par. Let me repeat also that unless there is such an aggregate demand, that is, tight employment, the necessary incentives to acquire the experience, training and even schooling which are the sources of the more valuable skills will be blunted, thwarted, and even nullified.

Definition of Skills. The concept of skills in this context includes

[11] Bureau of the Census, *Population Characteristics, Negro Population, March 1964,* Series P-20, No. 142, October 11, 1965, Table 1.

[12] I do not wish to imply by "economic equilibrium" that there exists a single once-and-for-all adjustment. As the economy adjusts, additional developments occur which then call for additional and perhaps quite different adjustments. Thus adjustment is a process and not a discrete move in response to a particular existing maladjustment. The search here is for policies, institutions, and mechanisms which will be efficient in producing the adjustment process.

all human capabilities that are valuable in activities pertaining to production. Thus capabilities that enter into consumption are omitted, although as a rule they, too, improve as a consequence of investment activities that increase the productive skills of a people. The skills that contribute to production are partly innate (inherited) and partly acquired; our concern here is restricted to those that are acquired. Their economic value is determined by demand for and supply of skills. It should be noted also that particular skills, although years have been spent in acquiring them, may become a drug on the market. The demand for farming skills is contracting, and these particular skills are in excess supply. Moreover, our type of economic growth causes all manner of skills to become obsolete, a process which has given rise to the statement that most persons during their working years face the prospect of changing occupations two or more times. Then, too, the value of a skill depends in part on its location; that is, a person with a particular skill must not only find where that skill is in demand but he must also be prepared to work at that location. Thus an essential part of the investment in skills is the cost of acquiring job information and the cost of migrating to the place where the appropriate job is to be had.[13] Since acquired skills can be ranked according to their economic value, it will be convenient to refer to those that fetch relatively high earnings as *high skills* and, conversely, to those that are associated with relatively low earnings as *low skills*. By this standard, as already noted, marketable skills of most Negroes rank very low, and so do the skills of most persons in the farm labor force regardless of color.

Functional Distribution of Income. When it comes to integrating functional and personal distribution of income, economic theory is not helpful. Even so we know some salient features underlying particular changes over time in the distribution of income. It becomes more unequal when relatively large numbers of young workers enter upon employment, when the proportion of women in the labor force increases, and when cyclical unemployment is on the rise. It becomes more equal as an economy moves toward and maintains a lower rate of unemployment than formerly, as the cost of mobility, including job

[13] See special supplement of the *Journal of Political Economy,* "Investment in Human Beings," Vol. 70, October 1962, papers by Larry A. Sjaastad and George J. Stigler.

information, falls, and of major importance as the schooling of the labor force rises. Increases in on-the-job training presumably would also reduce the inequality of the personal distribution of income.

By all accounts the functional share of income from property has been declining.[14] The stock of tangible reproducible wealth has not increased at so high a rate as the acquired abilities of workers. Differences in the private rates of return have favored investment in human capital. True, the relative decline in income from material wealth would undoubtedly have been somewhat less during the recent past had the tax on corporate income remained at the prewar level. Meanwhile, what has been happening to the personal distribution of wealth holdings? It is hard to believe that laborers have been acquiring a substantially larger share of his wealth and that it is the source that has brought about the observed rise in their income. The stock of wealth represented by houses may be an exception, in the sense that it has been an attractive investment for many families of laborers while the economy has been adjusting to the favorable tax treatment that home ownership has been receiving. But homes owned by families with less than $3,000 of income in 1962 had a mean value of only $3,750. Any plausible increase in the net worth of low-income workers since the mid-thirties could account for only a very small part of the decline in the proportion of families falling below, say, $3,000.

Meanwhile, labor's functional share of national income has been rising. The demand for workers with high skills has been increasing at a higher rate than that for workers with low skills. The incentive to increase skills has been strong and the supply of skills has been responding for people have been investing much more than formerly to increase their skills. But why has the demand for skills been shifting upward in this manner? In my judgment it has come about mainly as a consequence of the dynamic process in which skills along with new useful knowledge gradually have been increasing national income. At the same time the resulting rise in per capita income of consumers has altered the mix of products and services demanded in

[14] Here I follow closely a part of my paper, "Public Approaches to Minimize Poverty," in *Poverty Amid Affluence,* edited by Leo Fishman, Yale University Press, 1966.

such a way that the products and services requiring high skills have increased at a higher rate than those requiring low skills. Another factor in this process has undoubtedly been the increase in the demand for producer durables and services by the military establishment, which also has been increasing the demand for high skills.

Three Testable Hypotheses. In analyzing investment in human capital, whether in farm people or in human beings in general, it is necessary to specify, identify, and where possible estimate the magnitude of the factors that alter the demand for and supply of productive skills. The cost of acquiring skills and the returns from them are essential parts of the analysis. The rate of return may be positive, yet so low that the investment is not warranted either on private or public account because alternative investment opportunities may be better than these.

Savings from income and the investment of them in response to rates of return can alternatively be viewed as a process of acquiring income streams in response to the price(s) of the sources of these income streams. The latter formulation has the marked advantage that we can straightaway apply the concepts of demand and supply to determine the price of alternative sources of (permanent) income streams. An income stream can be given quantitative dimensions per unit of time, that is, a one-dollar-per-year income stream. Except for income transfers, to obtain possession of an income stream it is necessary to acquire the source of that stream. These sources are valuable, and each income stream in this sense has a price. The price may be high or low, and it may be rising or falling over time.

The underlying assumptions are the following: The sources of income streams are acquired at particular prices; these prices change over time; and people respond to changes in these prices subject to the restraints of the capital market, their preferences and capacity to save, the effects of taxes and subsidies and of discrimination with respect to employment and investment. We can then postulate a dynamic process and derive the following complementary hypotheses that pertain to our type of economic growth of recent decades.[15]

[15] Here I follow closely my paper, "Investing in Poor People: An Economist's View," *American Economic Review,* Vol. 60, May 1965, pp. 510-20.

1. The price of the sources of income streams that represent the acquired human capabilities of value in economic endeavor declined during this period relative to the price of material forms.

2. In responding to this change in the relative prices of these two sources of income the rate of investment in human sources rose during this period relative to that in material sources.

3. The increase in the investment in human sources relative to the investment in nonhuman sources has increased earnings relative to property income, and the more equal distribution of investment in men has tended to equalize earnings among human agents.

These are testable hypotheses, which appear to win support from a number of new studies. The private rates of return to schooling support the first. My attempt to test the second hypothesis, admittedly a very rough approximation of the increases in the last two of these stocks, indicates for the period between 1929 and 1957 that the stock of reproducible tangible wealth increased at an annual rate of about 2 percent whereas that of education in the labor force rose at a rate of 4 percent, and that of on-the-job training of males in the labor force at over 5 percent. The marked increase in the proportion of the labor force that has attended high school and college is one of the developments in support of the third hypothesis.

The long-run changes in the supply of the sources of income streams may be explored either in terms of adjustments to shifts in the demand or in terms of factors which play a fairly independent role. The adjustment process in which demand and supply interact is the core of the economic behavior underlying the formulation of the second hypothesis here advanced. The major "independent" factors affecting the supply are as follows: research and development activities and the acquisition of a part of the resulting useful knowledge by people, the mobility (immobility) of labor in leaving declining industries and occupations, the amount and distribution of public investment in schooling, and, closely related, the discrimination against Negroes, rural farm children, and others with respect to schooling.

Implications. The first and most general implication is that the real earnings of workers have been rising because the demand for high skills has been increasing relative to that for low skills and because workers have been acquiring the more valuable skills.

Another implication is that the earnings of particular classes of workers, including farm workers, are relatively low because the demand for their skills has been declining. Although workers generally have been responding to increases in the demands for high skills, workers in the farm labor force have not responded. The reasons for their lack of response are fairly obvious: unemployment, the adverse incidences of economic growth on some sectors, inadequate information, and a lack of opportunity to invest in acquiring the more valuable skills because of discrimination and the restraints on the capital market in providing funds for this purpose. In this connection, several of the arguments advanced earlier in this chapter are applicable and may be summarized as follows:

1. The market for the skills that are required in agriculture has long been depressed. The oldest members of the farm labor force have no real alternative but to settle for the depressed, salvage value of the skills they possess. Concealed here is the fact that in many farm communities the quality of elementary and secondary schooling has been and continues to be far below par, and thus the oncoming generation from these areas is ill-prepared to take advantage of the strong market in other parts of the economy for high skills. It should also be said that the vast expenditures by the federal government on behalf of agriculture have not been used to raise the level of these skills; on the contrary, they have been used in ways that enhance the income from some classes of property and worsen the personal distribution of income among farm families. Thus it should not come as a surprise that although farm families are presently a very small fraction of all United States families, they account for much of the observed poverty, and that many of the families in urban areas, whose learning capacity is very low have recently come from our farms.

2. The economic value of the skills of Negroes is lower still. In addition, both on our farms and in our cities, there has been and continues to be much job discrimination. But most important is the low level of the skills of Negroes, which is mainly a consequence of the history of discrimination against Negroes in schooling. Not only have Negroes obtained fewer years of schooling, but the schooling has been of very low quality, and especially so for the older Negroes in the labor force.

3. The South is burdened with lower earnings for work than other regions basically for three reasons: (1) It is more dependent on agriculture than the rest of the United States (it accounted for over 45 percent of all United States farms at the time the 1959 census of agriculture was taken); (2) the labor force in the South is more largely Negro than in the North and West and in terms of marketable skills the Negroes in the South are even worse off than the Negroes in other regions; and (3) relatively more of the whites in the labor force in the South have low skills than whites in other regions. In short, the South has been lagging seriously in providing people the opportunities to invest in acquiring the high skills for which the demand has been increasing at so rapid a rate, predominantly because of social, political, and economic discrimination adverse to poor people.

Related Findings and Additional Implications. I shall refer, at last, to some recent work on the economics of education that is relevant here.

1. In a study, Micha Gisser,[16] while at Chicago, developed an approach to estimate the "two effects of additional schooling on the effective supply of human agents committed to farming, that is, (1) the out-migration effect reducing the supply and (2) the capability effect increasing the supply." His estimates for the United States show that both effects are substantial but that the out-migration effect is appreciably larger than the capability effect. He found that an increase in the level of schooling in rural farm areas of 10 percent will induce a 6 to 7 percent additional migration out of agriculture and in terms of the net effect it will raise the farm wage rate 5 percent.[17]

2. Griliches' studies [18] to determine the sources of gains in agricultural productivity show that the schooling of the farm labor force is a significant variable in determining the labor input. He found that the *quality* of this labor measured by schooling is as important as the

[16] Micha Gisser, "Some Implications of Schooling and the Farm Problem," Paper 6305, Agricultural Economics Research Series, University of Chicago, July 18, 1963.

[17] Micha Gisser, "Schooling and the Farm Problem," *Econometrica,* Vol. 33, No. 3, July 1965, pp. 582–92.

[18] Zvi Griliches, "Research Expenditures, Education, and the Aggregate Agricultural Production Function," *American Economic Review,* Vol. 54, December 1964, pp. 961–74. Also, see his earlier studies listed under "References" in the paper cited.

quantity measured by the size of the farm labor force. Furthermore, when "adjustments are made to bring the farm and nonfarm labor force measures into comparable units," he found "that a ratio of about 0.7 of farm to urban per capita income is consistent with equal returns for comparable labor." He also calls attention to the fact that "There is some indication that the marginal return to the quality of labor in agriculture may actually exceed the opportunity cost in the nonagricultural sector." Griliches' estimate of the marginal product of schooling in agriculture in 1959 is $1.30 per dollar of cost.

3. Gisser in his Ph.D. research [19] found that the rate of *returns* to schooling in agriculture, when he included both earnings foregone and all school expenditure as costs, and when he took farm wages as a measure of earnings—adding a year of schooling to the median years completed by males as of 1958—were as follows:

Region	*Rate of Return (in percent)*
West and Southwest	20
North Atlantic	21
East and West Central and Plains	23
Southeast	28

4. The first study to identify and measure the economic value of the differences in the quality of schooling of males in the farm labor force has been completed by Finis Welch at Chicago. It is not premature to indicate that these differences in the quality of schooling are exceedingly important in determining the real level of skills and the associated economic productivity of farm labor, hired and self-employed.

[19] Micha Gisser, *Schooling and the Agricultural Labor Force,* Ph.D. dissertation in Economics, University of Chicago, 1961.

[5]

Occupational Mobility from the Farm Labor Force

DALE E. HATHAWAY

The continued need for occupational mobility of farm people is evident in the low return to human effort in agriculture and the future prospects that even less labor will be needed in agriculture. Both points have been well established by others. Therefore, it is enough here merely to point out that we need to know more about the processes of occupational mobility so that we may take actions that will enable those processes to work better. While occupational mobility obviously is occurring now and has been for the life of our country, it is also obvious that serious impediments to mobility remain, and new ones may be arising. These impediments account in part for the failure of the returns to labor in agriculture to rise relative to those in nonagricultural pursuits.

In this paper I shall discuss four central issues relating to occupational mobility from agriculture. They are:

1. How does occupational mobility take place?
2. What are the factors influencing occupational mobility of rural people?
3. How does the labor market work for rural people?
4. What are the implications of the preceding issues for public and private policy?

In discussing these issues I shall draw widely upon the research of others on the subject, and I shall deal with rural people in general

---

DALE E. HATHAWAY is a professor in the Department of Agricultural Economics at Michigan State University. His paper has benefited from the comments of Dr. Arley Waldo and W. Keith Bryant, Department of Agricultural Economics, University of Minnesota, and Dr. Brian Perkins, College of Agriculture, University of Guelph.

rather than limit the discussion to hired farm workers, farm operators, or some other narrow category, although many illustrations will deal with specific categories. I believe it is important to deal with rural people inasmuch as the farm labor problem cannot be realistically separated from the labor mobility problem of the entire rural population. To completely separate the farm work force and the rural labor force assumes a compartmentalization within the rural labor force that does not exist and can be misleading at times.

HOW OCCUPATIONAL MOBILITY OCCURS

One of the most important factors leading to a reduction in the farm work force is not occupational mobility in the true sense. This is the occupational mobility that occurs from one generation of the labor force to the next. It typically occurs when rural young people enter the labor force, and the difference between the retirement rate from the farm labor force and the rate of new entry to the farm labor force is the most significant factor leading to a reduction in the number of persons employed in agriculture. Because of the relatively advanced age of the farm operator labor force the difference between retirement and entry rate will continue to be of major importance in the future reduction of the farm operator labor force.

The hired farm work force is much younger, with a median age of 25.3 years in 1964.[1] Even if we exclude the casual workers (less than 25 days of farm work), 43 percent of the regular workers were under 25 years old and 58 percent were under 35 years old.[2] Thus, with so few near retirement age, the difference between entrants and retirements is not going to reduce sharply the hired farm labor force. Therefore, we must be concerned especially with occupational mobility from farm work to nonfarm work if the hired farm labor force is to be reduced sufficiently to bring the earnings of its members into line with the earnings of nonfarm workers.

Although the remainder of this paper deals with occupational mo-

[1] Gladys K. Bowles, *The Hired Farm Work Force of 1964,* Agricultural Economic Report 82, USDA, ERS, August 1965.

[2] *Ibid.,* Table 4, p. 11.

bility of persons out of the farm labor force, the importance of increasing the opportunities of rural youth to enter the *nonfarm* labor force at the time they enter the active labor force cannot be overemphasized. The easiest and best way to bring adjustments in the farm labor force is at this point, and all subsequent adjustments are likely to involve greater social and economic costs.

Most of our statistics measure the numbers of persons employed in an occupation or industry at a given point in time, and there is a tendency to assume that the net changes shown by changes in absolute numbers over time are the result of a relatively simple transfer process whereby persons move from one occupation to another. If, however, we look at the employment record of a given set of individuals over a period of time the picture appears quite different.[3] We find, for instance, that the gross occupational mobility out of the farm work force is very high. At the same time there is a substantial back movement into the farm work force so that the net reduction in most years is small (Table 1). In fact at least one year in the late 1950s it appears there may have been a net inflow into the farm work force.

This extensive movement back and forth does not appear to be the result of a small group of highly mobile workers in the hired farm labor force. Despite the long tenure in their current jobs (18.0 years) found in a study of *Job Tenure of American Workers*,[4] Social Security data indicate significant occupational mobility out of and into agricultural employment for both farm operators and hired laborers.[5] Thus occupational mobility is not a continuous, smooth, one-way process that works well for everyone. Instead, it appears to be a process of trial and error adjustment to individual situations of uncertainty and imperfect knowledge.

Turning to those persons who are in the farm labor force, either as self-employed farm operators or as hired farm workers, we ask how occupational mobility from farming takes place. Do such individuals

[3] Brian B. Perkins, *Labor Mobility between the Farm and Nonfarm Sector,* Unpublished Ph.D. thesis, Michigan State University, 1964.

[4] Harvey R. Hamel, *Job Tenure of American Workers, January 1963,* Advance Summary, Special Labor Force Report.

[5] Perkins, *Labor Mobility between the Farm and Nonfarm Sector,* Chapter IV.

decide suddenly one day to leave agricultural employment and, having severed their ties in agriculture, present themselves for nonfarm employment? The answer to the question would appear to be no, for the process of occupational mobility for the farm labor force seems to be gradual and uncertain and works unsatisfactorily for many of the participants in the process. It appears that the process of occupational mobility from the farm labor force most often occurs via the route of multiple job holding, where the individual has a part-time job in the nonfarm labor force for a year or more.

Table 1 A Comparison of Mobility Rates and Nonfarm Unemployment Rates, 1955–59 [a]

	Mobility Period			
	1955–56	*1956–57*	*1957–58*	*1958–59*
Based on all Persons in Social Security Sample	*Percentage of Farm Labor Force in Beginning Year That Participated in Occupation Mobility*			
Off-farm rate	14.6	15.6	12.5	13.8
In-farm rate	13.3	10.7	14.3	11.7
Net % change in beginning farm labor force	−1.3	−4.9	+1.8	+2.1
Based on Persons in Sample with Coverage in All Years 1955–59				
Off-farm rate	17.5	18.1	13.3	14.0
In-farm rate	14.8	11.8	15.0	12.2
Net % change in beginning farm labor force	−2.7	−6.3	+1.7	−1.8
Unemployment Rate in Nonfarm Labor Force [a]	4.2	4.3	6.3	5.5

[a] The unemployment rates refer to the second year of each period. Computed from employment statistics published in *The Economic Report of the President,* January 1963.

Source: Adapted from Brian Perkins and Dale Hathaway, *The Movement of Labor between Farm and Nonfarm Jobs,* Research Bulletin 13, Michigan State University, 1966, Table 17.

Annual surveys of the Bureau of Census, the Census of Agriculture, and other data on multiple job holding tend to show an almost constant proportion of farm operators and hired farm workers who have nonfarm as well as farm employment. Because of the relatively constant percentage of such persons it often has been assumed that these persons are permanently in this status. Continuous register data, such as Social Security data, give quite a different picture, however. They show that although the proportion of the farm labor force employed in nonfarm industries is relatively constant, the persons so employed are not the same ones.[6] About 60 percent of all farm operators covered by Social Security as farm operators in 1955 had some current or previous nonfarm employment coverage; only 6 percent were multiple job holders for five consecutive years during the period 1955–59.[7]

Perkins' found conclusive evidence that multiple job holding is a major factor in occupational mobility for both self-employed farm operators and hired farm workers.[8] He found that the farm-nonfarm occupational mobility rate for multiple job-holding farm operators in 1955–59 was over six times that of farm operators not holding nonfarm jobs, and the mobility rate for multiple job-holding farm wage workers was over four times as high as for farm wage workers not holding nonfarm jobs in the beginning year. Moreover, for both farm operators and wage workers the mobility rates rose directly with the number of years of nonfarm job experiences in the previous three years.

Thus a major link in the occupational mobility out of agriculture appears to be via the process of multiple job holding. This is not surprising in a sense, for success begets success. If we can show a prospective nonfarm employer previous nonfarm work experience, the chances for nonfarm employment undoubtedly are improved. Equally important, if we have some satisfactory experience in nonfarm employment, the personal uncertainty of leaving agricultural employment for the nonfarm labor market is reduced. Therefore, the use of multiple job holding as a method of testing the water before plunging

[6] Arley D. Waldo, *The Off-Farm Employment of Farm Operators In the United States,* Unpublished Ph.D. thesis, Michigan State University, 1962. Dale E. Hathaway and Arley D. Waldo, *Multiple Jobholding by Farm Operators,* Research Bulletin 5, Michigan State University Agricultural Experiment Station, East Lansing, 1964.

[7] Hathaway and Waldo, *Multiple Jobholding by Farm Operators,* Table 5, p. 15, and Uel Blank, *OASI Data of the Farm Work Force,* Unpublished Ph.D. thesis, Michigan State University, 1960, p. 183.

[8] Perkins, *Labor Mobility between the Farm and Nonfarm Sector,* Table V-2.

in over our head is understandable, but it also raises some major questions.

First, the entry to nonfarm employment via multiple job holding means entry to a labor market that is relatively restricted geographically, at least for farm operators and permanent farm wage workers. It is less restrictive in this regard for migratory farm wage workers, but even these persons are most likely to enter the rural or small-town labor market rather than the large urban markets. As I shall show later this results in more sharply differing patterns of employment and earnings than we find in the large urban labor markets.

Although discussion on migration from farming usually is on matters of long-distance migration from rural areas to large urban centers, most of the evidence from surveys suggests that most rural people migrate relatively short distances when changing occupations. Long-distance rural-urban migration is primarily a phenomenon of the young nonwhites leaving the South, and it sometimes obscures the more common situation regarding farm-nonfarm occupation mobility.[9]

We might regard the multiple job-holding route of occupational mobility as an individualistic ad hoc method of achieving nonfarm job skills, a type of personal unemployment insurance against the uncertainty facing a new entrant to the nonfarm labor market, an individual employment service testing and guidance system for personal job preference evaluations, and a personal insurance of some social stability. There is ample evidence, however, that at least on the agricultural side this type of arrangement is far from optimal, inasmuch as it retards rather than encourages the necessary restructuring of agriculture. It also severely restricts the kind of labor market which farm people enter. Thus we can ask whether there may not be more efficient and desirable ways for farm people to get nonfarm skills,

[9] In this regard see Harold Guither, "Factors Influencing Decisions to Leave Farming," *Journal of Farm Economics,* Vol. 45, No. 3, August 1963, pp. 567-76. His study supports both the limited geographical and multiple job holding thesis regarding occupational mobility. Also see Calvin L. Beale, John C. Hudson, and Vera J. Banks, *Characteristics of the U. S. Population by Farm and Nonfarm Origin,* Agricultural Economics Report 66, Economic Research Service, USDA, December 1964, Table 5, which shows that 79 to 95 percent of the farm-born persons are residing in the region where they were born.

achieve economic security while changing occupations, and get guidance and experience in nonfarm work. The development of ways to provide these vital services would appear to be the responsibility of the Department of Labor.

FACTORS INFLUENCING OCCUPATIONAL MOBILITY

In general, the factors influencing occupational mobility from the farm labor force might be summed up by saying that opportunity for economic improvement is the primary factor motivating occupational mobility. There appear to be several factors that influence this opportunity for improvement. Some of them are related to the general employment level, the location of the individual, and the occupational and industrial structure. Some are related to individual worker characteristics of age, education, sex, and race.

Unemployment and Mobility. One of the most important aspects of opportunity for occupational mobility out of the farm work force is related to the overall level of nonfarm unemployment. Although this effect has been commented on before, it had not been well documented until the Perkins study of Social Security data. Table 1 shows the occupation mobility rates out of and into the farm work force for a 5-year period covering a vigorous business expansion and a sharp recession which markedly increased the nonfarm unemployment rate. These data indicate there was an actual net inflow into the farm work force during the year of highest unemployment. The inflow was especially marked by a return of farm operators to farming.

What is not shown in this table but was evident in the data was that the rate of entry into the farm work force by rural young people also increased as nonfarm unemployment rose. Thus nonfarm unemployment affects the size of the farm work force in three ways: (1) It reduces the rate of occupational mobility out of farming; (2) it increases the rate of back movement from nonfarm to farm jobs; and (3) it increases the rate of new entrants to farming as rural youth find nonfarm opportunities limited.

In examining the impact of nonfarm unemployment on the off-farm mobility rates of various groups, it appears that the greatest impact was to reduce the occupational mobility of the younger age groups significantly. The decline apparently affected farm operators and hired farm workers and whites and nonwhites about the same. As mentioned earlier, however, the back movement of farm operators was higher, presumably because they had somewhere to go.

Another issue is the effect of local unemployment on the earnings of rural farm families and of farmers and farm managers. Surprisingly, Bryant found that outside the South local unemployment did not depress the income level of *farm families*.[10] However, local unemployment was a major factor depressing the *earnings* of *farm managers* for the United States and in most regions. Outside the South the labor market for rural males and rural females is apparently quite differentiated, so that local male unemployment does not affect total rural farm family incomes. In the South, however, there appears to be considerable competition between males and females in the unskilled labor market so that local unemployment depresses family income as well as the earnings of farmers.

Thus it is clear that nonfarm unemployment depresses the earnings of labor in agriculture. It does so because it results in a reduction in the rate of outflow from agriculture and because it increases the rate of outflow from agriculture and increases the rate of backflow into the farm labor force. Since labor mobility within agriculture is relatively limited, especially among farm operators, and since so much farm-nonfarm occupational mobility is local there is a direct relationship between local unemployment and farm earnings as well as an aggregate impact upon occupational mobility out of the farm work force.

Location and Mobility. It has been suggested that occupational mobility out of farming is facilitated by location relative to large urban industrial centers.[11] Moreover, it has been suggested that this mobility will result in higher earnings in agriculture adjacent to such cen-

[10] Wilfrid Keith Bryant, *An Analysis of Inter-Community Income Differentials in Agriculture in the United States,* Unpublished Ph. D. thesis, Michigan State University, 1963.

[11] T. W. Schultz, *Economic Organization of Agriculture,* McGraw-Hill Book Co., New York, 1953.

ters because of the better operation of the factor (labor) market. Recent analyses throw additional light upon these relationships.

An analysis of the occupation distribution of residents by distance from the nearest Standard Metropolitan Statistical Areas (SMSA) and taking into account the size of the SMSA indicate a strong relationship between the occupation distribution of rural farm males and their proximity to large cities (Table 2). For instance, white rural males were more frequently employed as salesmen in areas close to SMSA's, and, moreover, there was a positive relationship between city size and the frequency of such employment. Some relationship between location and occupation distribution was found for white rural farm males for 17 out of 21 occupation classifications tested. Such relationships could occur (1) because the total occupation mix varies according to distance from cities or (2) because rural farm males have different competitive positions in different labor markets. If the occupation structure of rural males was due to the first reason, the same relationships between occupation structure and location should exist for all males in a given area (rural farm, rural nonfarm, or urban). But they do not. Only in the case of metal craftsmen and operatives in nondurable manufacturing do we find the same relationship for all residence groups and races.

The occupational distribution of white rural farm males is the group most affected by location. White rural nonfarm males did not differ markedly from urban males in this regard. Surprisingly, the occupation distribution of nonwhite males in all residence groups appears much less related to distance than white males are.

If we take city size as well as distance into account, most of the differences between rural and urban males and whites and nonwhites disappear, except for the significantly less frequent relationship between occupation distribution for nonwhite rural farm males.[12]

These observations can be summed up as follows. Around very large cities the entire male occupational structure is related to proximity to the city. Around smaller cities, however, the occupational structure for rural males is the one most affected by location, suggesting that the relatively thin nonfarm labor markets around smaller

[12] I suspect this is due to the very small numbers of nonwhite rural farm males near the largest cities, which are located primarily outside the South.

Table 2 The Relationship between Residence Classification, Race, and Proximity to Cities and Occupation Distribution of Employed Males in 1960

Occupation	*RF White Males*	*RNF White Males*	*Urban White Males*	*RF NW Males*	*RNF NW Males*	*Urban NW Males*	*RF White Males*	*RNF White Males*	*Urban NW Males*	*RF NW Males*	*RNF NW Males*	*Urban NW Males*
			Distance						*Size-Distance*			
Professional, technical, kindred	+	0	0	0	—	0	+	+	0	0	+	0
Farmers and farm managers	—	—	—	0	0	—	—	—	—	—	—	—
Mgrs., officials, proprietors	+	—	—	0	0	—	+	—	—	0	+	0
Clerical, kindred	+	+	0	0	—	0	+	+	+	+	+	+
Sales workers	+	+	0	0	—	0	+	+	0	0	0	+
Foremen	+	0	0	0	—	0	+	+	+	0	+	+
Mechanics	+	+	—	0	0	0	+	+	—	0	+	+
Metal craftsmen	+	+	+	+	+	+	+	+	+	0	+	+
Const. craftsmen	+	+	—	0	0	0	0	0	—	0	0	—
Other craftsmen	+	0	0	0	—	0	+	0	0	0	+	0
Cpt., drivers	+	0	—	+	+	+	0	—	—	0	—	—
Cpt., durable manufactures	+	+	+	0	+	0	+	+	+	0	0	+

Cpt., nondurable manufactures	+	+	+	+	+	+	0	0	0	0	0	0
Cpt., nonmanufactures	0	—	—	0	0	0	0	—	—	0	0	—
Priv. household	0	0	0	+	+	0	+	+	0	0	+	0
Service workers	+	—	0	0	0	0	+	0	0	0	+	0
Farm laborers	—	—	0	0	0	0	0	—	—	0	—	—
Const. laborers	+	0	—	0	0	0	+	—	—	0	0	—
Mfg. laborers	+	0	0	+	0	0	0	0	+	0	—	0
Other laborers	0	—	—	0	0	0	+	—	—	0	0	—
Occupation not reported	+	+	+	—	0	0	+	+	+	0	+	+
No. occupations related to proximity	17	13	11	5	9	5	14	15	14	2	13	13

Code: A plus sign (+) means there was a significant positive relationship between the proportion of the labor force employed in the occupation and proximity to an urban area. A negative sign (—) means the relationship between the proportion employed in the occupation and proximity was significantly negative. A zero (0) means there was no significant relationship between proximity and the proportion employed in the occupation. Significance was determined by testing the perimeters of regressions between occupation and the distance or size-distance variable, using the "t" test at the .05 level.

Source: D. E. Hathaway, J. Allan Beegle, and W. Keith Bryant, *Rural America,* book to be published in 1966 as part of Census Monograph Series, Chapter 6.

cities and towns tend to affect adversely the occupations available to farm males seeking nonfarm employment and to limit their prospects for entering the more desirable nonfarm occupations.

For females the situation appears quite different (Table 3). The occupational structure of all residence groups and both races seems much less sensitive to location relative to cities over 50,000 population than was the case for males. The strongest relationships were found to be between city size and distance and the occupational distribution of urban females. Thus the labor market for rural females appears less related to location than is the case for males.

Despite the strong relationship between occupation distribution and location for rural farm males, however, there is no apparent relationship between either the relative or the absolute income level in farming and location.

The differences in earnings of two occupation groups—operatives and farmers and farm managers—do not increase with distance from SMSA's.[13] Indeed, except for the South and the Great Plains, the earnings differentials between these occupations are such that farmers would be about as well off to take local jobs as operatives as to migrate to SMSA's if this is the primary occupation for which they can qualify. However, migration offers them a wider range of occupations than they would obtain locally.

Finally, there is no consistent relationship between proximity to a large city and the earnings of farmers and farm managers.[14] Despite the indication that the occupation structure of rural farm males is strongly related to location, the differential in earnings is not, and the relationship with respect to location and earnings within agriculture is very mixed. On the basis of data presently available there is little evidence to support the thesis that location is a prime factor in occupation mobility and/or earnings of farm workers. However, location may be very important in determining the occupation mix available to those moving from agriculture.

[13] D. E. Hathaway, "Urban-Industrial Development and Income Differentials between Occupations," *Journal of Farm Economics,* Vol. 46, February 1964, pp. 56–66.

[14] W. K. Bryant, *An Analysis of Inter-Community Income Differentials in Agriculture in the United States,* Unpublished Ph.D. thesis, Michigan State University, 1963.

Table 3 The Relationship between Residence Classification, Race, and Proximity to Cities and Occupation of Employed Females in 1960

	White Females						*Nonwhite Females*					
	Distance			*Size-Distance*			*Distance*			*Size-Distance*		
	Rural Farm	*Rural Non-farm*	*Urban*	*Rural Farm*	*Rural Non-farm*	*Urban*	*Rural Farm*	*Rural Non-farm*	*Urban*	*Rural Farm*	*Rural Non-farm*	*Urban*
Professional, technical, kindred	0	—	—	0	0	—	0	—	0	0	0	—
Farmers and farm managers	—	0	0	—	—	—	0	0	0	—	—	0
Managers, officials, and proprietors	0	—	—	0	—	—	0	—	—	0	0	—
Clerical and kindred	+	0	0	+	+	0	0	—	0	0	+	+
Sales workers	0	—	0	—	—	+	0	—	—	0	0	+
Craftsmen, foremen, and kindred	+	+	+	0	+	+	+	0	0	0	0	+
Cpt., durable manufactures	+	+	+	+	+	+	0	0	0	0	+	+
Cpt., nondurable manufactures	0	+	+	0	0	0	0	+	+	+	0	+
Cpt., nonmanufactures	0	—	—	—	—	—	0	0	0	0	0	+
Private household	0	—	—	+	0	—	+	+	0	0	—	—
Service workers	0	—	—	0	—	—	0	0	—	0	+	+
Farm laborers	—	0	0	0	—	—	0	0	0	—	—	—
Laborers	+	0	0	0	0	+	—	—	0	0	0	+
Occupation not reported	0	+	+	0	+	+	—	—	0	0	+	+
No. occupations related to proximity	6	9	8	6	9	11	3	7	4	3	6	12

Code: A plus sign (+) means there was a significant positive relationship between the proportion of the labor force employed in the occupation and proximity to an urban area. A negative sign (—) means the relationship between the proportion employed in the occupation and proximity was significantly negative. A zero (0) means there was no significant relationship between proximity and the proportion employed in the occupation. Significance was determined by testing the perimeters of regressions between occupation and the distance or size-distance variable, using the "t" test at the .05 level.

Source: D. E. Hathaway, J. Allan Beegle, and W. Keith Bryant, *Rural America,* book to be published in 1966 as part of Census Monograph Series, Chapter 6.

HOW DOES THE LABOR MARKET OPERATE FOR THE FARM WORK FORCE?

The questions to be dealt with here relate mainly to how the labor market functions for farm people engaged in occupational mobility from the farm work force. Some of the issues are: What kind of occupational mobility do farm people achieve in today's labor market, why do so many who move to nonfarm employment return to farm work, and are there any obvious barriers to entry that retard occupational mobility from farm work?

One test of the occupational mobility out of agriculture is to look at the occupations of rural males who are employed outside the agricultural industry. It appears safe to assume that most persons classified as rural farm residents generally are or have been employed in agriculture, especially as farm operators. Because the rural nonfarm population is so heterogeneous, containing many urban fringe residents in the Northeast and Midwest, it is not correct to assume that most rural nonfarm residents have had any past association with farm employment.[19]

Table 5 shows the nonagricultural occupation distribution by residence, sex, and color in 1960. The occupation distribution of rural males is heavily skewed toward the lower-paying, less skilled occupations. For instance, about 42 percent of the white rural farm males and 68 percent of the nonwhite rural farm males work as operatives or laborers, compared to about one-quarter of white urban males in these two occupations.

Except for a lower proportion employed in clerical work and a higher proportion employed as operatives the sharp differences in occupational structure do not appear for white rural farm females. However, almost all nonwhite rural farm females are concentrated in three occupations—private household workers, service workers, and operatives. Thus it appears that the labor market functions to place most rural farm males in the less desirable nonfarm occupations, and this

[19] See D. E. Hathaway, J. Allan Beegle, and W. Keith Bryant, *Rural America,* for a discussion of the characteristics of the rural nonfarm population.

Table 5 Occupational Distribution of Persons Employed Outside Agriculture by Color and Sex, for U.S., Urban and Rural, 1960

	White				*Nonwhite*			
	U.S.	*Urban*	*Rural Nonfarm*	*Rural Farm*	*U.S.*	*Urban*	*Rural Nonfarm*	*Rural Farm*
Male								
Total, excl. farmers, farm mgrs., farm laborers, and farm foremen	100.0	100.0	100.0	100.0	100.0	100.0	100.0	100.0
Mgrs., officials, and proprietors	12.5	13.0	11.2	9.0	2.6	2.7	1.8	1.4
Clerical and kindred	7.7	8.5	5.2	5.4	5.7	6.5	1.7	1.4
Sales workers	8.0	8.7	5.9	5.2	1.7	1.9	0.9	1.0
Craftsmen, foremen, and kindred	22.2	21.4	25.3	23.0	11.5	11.5	11.3	10.4
Operatives and kindred	21.2	19.3	26.5	31.3	26.5	24.8	31.5	36.1
Private household	0.1	0.1	0.1	0.1	0.8	0.8	0.9	1.0
Service workers, excl. private household	5.6	6.1	4.5	3.5	15.5	16.8	9.4	6.2
Laborers, excl. farm and mine	6.1	5.2	8.6	10.6	21.9	19.7	33.3	31.8
Occupation not reported	4.5	4.7	3.9	6.1	9.5	10.1	5.9	8.3
Female								
Total, excl. farmers, farm mgrs., farm laborers, and farm foremen	100.0	100.0	100.0	100.0	100.0	100.0	100.0	100.0
Mgrs., officials, and proprietors	4.1	4.0	4.6	3.0	1.2	1.2	1.2	0.8
Clerical and kindred	33.2	35.7	24.4	22.2	8.8	9.9	2.6	1.7
Sales workers	8.8	8.9	8.7	8.0	1.8	1.9	1.2	1.3
Craftsmen, foremen, and kindred	1.3	1.3	1.2	1.2	0.7	0.8	0.4	0.3
Operatives and kindred	16.0	14.6	20.8	21.3	13.3	14.0	9.7	7.8
Private household	4.2	3.7	5.8	7.3	35.6	32.3	53.2	59.3
Service workers, excl. private household	12.6	11.8	15.8	13.7	21.5	22.2	18.0	13.0
Laborers, excl. farm and mine	0.5	0.4	0.7	0.6	1.0	0.9	1.2	1.2
Occupation not reported	5.4	5.5	4.8	6.1	8.4	8.9	5.0	5.5

also occurs for nonwhite rural farm females. Undoubtedly this is a function both of the personal characteristics of the individuals involved and of the relatively limited nonfarm labor market in most rural areas.

We can obtain two views of the industrial distribution of the nonfarm jobs taken by persons leaving agriculture. One view is obtained by examining the industry of employment of persons who left the farm labor force for nonfarm employment as indicated by Social Security data (Table 6). It shows that those leaving agriculture tend to

Table 6 The Industrial Distributions of Wage Jobs Taken by Movers in the 1956–57 and the 1957–58 Mobility Periods, by Farm Occupation of Movers [a]

	Farm Operators		*Farm Wage Workers*	
Industry	*1957*	*1958*	*1957*	*1958*
Agriculture,[b] forestry, and fisheries	2.7%	2.4%	8.9%	6.1%
Mining	4.2	2.6	2.8	2.2
Construction	15.2	14.8	16.1	19.2
Manufacturing	22.3	21.3	23.4	21.5
Utilities	4.5	4.9	4.7	5.3
Wholesale and retail trade	18.1	21.9	24.6	26.3
Finance, insurance, and real estate	2.3	2.4	1.7	1.7
Services	8.2	10.3	10.9	10.8
Government	21.1	17.9	4.8	5.3
Other [c]	1.3	1.5	2.1	1.4
All industries	100.0	100.0	100.0	100.0

[a] Distributions of movers' jobs based on Social Security sample data. Distribution of unskilled occupations in 1960 computed from Census of Population, PC (1), 1D, U.S.

[b] Excluding farm employment. [c] Including nonclassifiable and nonclassified.

Source: Brian Perkins and Dale Hathaway, *The Movement of Labor between Farm and Nonfarm Jobs,* adapted from Table 7.

enter manufacturing, construction, and wholesale and retail trade. In addition, an unusually high proportion of the farm operators taking nonfarm work enter government. Apart from government, the industrial distribution of farm operators who moved and hired farm work-

Table 7 Distribution of Employed Persons, by Color and Sex, Urban and Rural, for the U.S., 1960

	Total				*White*				*Nonwhite*			
	U.S.	*Urban*	*Rural Nonfarm*	*Rural Farm*	*U.S.*	*Urban*	*Rural Nonfarm*	*Rural Farm*	*U.S.*	*Urban*	*Rural Nonfarm*	*Rural Farm*
Male												
Total, excl. agriculture, forestry, and fisheries	100.0	100.0	100.0	100.0	100.0	100.0	100.0	100.0	100.0	100.0	100.0	100.0
Mining	1.7	1.0	4.0	2.9	1.8	1.0	4.1	3.0	0.6	0.3	2.5	1.2
Construction	9.2	8.1	12.5	15.0	9.1	8.0	12.4	15.0	10.0	9.3	13.6	15.9
Manufacturing	33.2	32.8	34.4	35.1	33.6	33.4	34.2	34.9	28.4	26.8	37.0	38.7
Transp., communications, and public utilities	9.3	9.5	8.7	8.5	7.1	9.5	8.7	8.5	9.3	9.6	7.9	8.5
Wholesale and retail trade	18.7	19.2	17.5	16.8	18.9	19.3	17.8	17.1	16.4	17.0	13.6	12.2
Finance, insurance, and real estate	3.7	4.2	2.1	1.7	3.9	4.4	2.2	1.8	2.0	2.2	0.7	0.4
Services	12.5	12.8	12.2	9.2	14.1	14.6	12.9	9.7	18.2	18.6	16.0	12.6
Government	5.8	6.1	4.6	4.9	5.7	2.4	4.7	5.1	6.6	7.2	3.7	2.3
All other	4.0	4.2	3.0	5.2	3.6	3.7	2.9	5.0	8.4	8.9	5.1	8.1
Female												
Total, excl. agriculture, forestry, and fisheries	100.0	100.0	100.0	100.0	100.0	100.0	100.0	100.0	100.0	100.0	100.0	100.0
Mining and construction	0.9	0.9	0.8	0.7	1.0	1.0	0.9	0.7	0.3	0.3	0.3	0.3
Manufacturing	21.2	20.6	23.8	22.8	22.8	22.1	25.4	24.5	9.7	10.3	6.7	4.9
Transp., communications, and Public utilities	3.7	4.0	2.8	2.6	4.1	4.4	3.0	2.8	1.1	1.2	0.5	0.6
Wholesale and retail trade	21.2	21.1	21.8	18.3	22.6	22.6	23.1	19.3	11.0	11.5	8.8	6.8
Finance, insurance, and real estate	5.9	6.5	3.7	3.7	6.5	7.2	4.0	4.0	1.7	1.9	0.5	0.3
Services	37.7	37.3	38.7	42.0	34.0	33.6	35.0	38.4	64.7	62.3	77.3	81.2
Government	4.4	4.4	4.4	4.6	4.5	4.4	4.7	5.0	3.9	4.3	1.4	0.6
All other	4.9	5.1	3.9	5.3	4.6	4.7	3.9	5.2	7.7	8.2	4.5	5.3

ers who moved was not as different as we might expect from looking at the occupation distributions.

Another view of the industrial distribution resulting from occupation mobility can be obtained by looking at the industrial distribution of the rural farm population in 1960 (Table 7). For all rural farm males, white and nonwhite, the high proportion employed in manufacturing is again obvious. In fact, it is even higher than the rate of entry to manufacturing, suggesting either that the rate of retention in manufacturing is higher or, more likely, that persons who experience geographical mobility as well as occupational mobility are more likely to find employment outside manufacturing. It appears that geographical mobility may be related to employment in the wholesale and retail trades.

There is little difference between the industry distribution of white rural females and their urban counterparts. All females are heavily concentrated in service industries, wholesale and retail trade, and manufacturing. Nonwhite females in all residence groups are heavily concentrated in service industries, with wholesale and retail trade a weak second. There appears to be a greater concentration in service industries among rural farm nonwhite females than for other residence groups.

There is also a differential in industry of nonfarm employment by age of the person at the time occupational mobility occurs. (Table 8 shows one year which appears representative.) Almost half of the younger farm operators who took nonfarm employment went into construction and manufacturing. Older farm operators tended to go into government and services. Similar differences, although somewhat less pronounced, were found for farm wage workers.

In a sense it appears that much of the occupational mobility may prove to be "out of the frying pan into the fire" in so far as the individuals involved are concerned. A very high proportion of the occupational mobility out of the farm labor force appears to be in unskilled occupations and into industries where, like agriculture, unskilled labor is rapidly being displaced by machines. Thus, as things seem to be working out, yesterday's underemployed in agriculture may become tomorrow's unemployed factory workers, twice displaced by the substitution of labor by capital.

Table 8 The Industrial Distributions of Wage Jobs Taken by Movers in the 1956–57 Mobility Period, by Farm Occupation of Movers and by Age [a]

(*In Percentages*)

	Farm Operators					Farm Wage Workers				
1957 Industry — *Age:*	*Under 25*	*25–34*	*35–44*	*45–54*	*55 and over*	*Under 25*	*25–34*	*35–44*	*45–54*	*55 and over*
Agriculture,[b] forestry, and fisheries	8.1%	2.2%	2.8%	3.1%	1.1%	9.7%	7.5%	5.7%	9.7%	11.9%
Mining	1.2	3.6	4.2	7.5	2.2	2.9	2.9	2.7	2.1	4.0
Construction	16.3	14.2	19.1	18.1	7.4	14.6	16.3	18.3	19.8	13.5
Manufacturing	31.4	29.9	24.1	20.8	11.0	24.7	25.5	24.3	20.9	12.7
Utilities	3.5	6.6	5.5	2.7	3.3	4.6	7.0	4.2	3.7	2.0
Wholesale and retail trade	16.3	20.1	16.1	17.4	20.6	27.0	23.1	23.8	21.9	23.0
Finance, insurance, and real estate	1.2	3.3	0.6	1.0	5.5	1.0	1.4	2.8	1.3	4.8
Services	7.0	5.5	10.8	4.8	11.4	9.5	9.6	11.6	12.0	19.4
Government	15.1	13.1	15.0	23.2	36.8	4.5	4.3	4.4	5.2	7.5
Other [c]	0	1.5	1.9	1.4	0.7	1.6	2.4	2.3	3.4	1.2
All industries	100.0	100.0	100.0	100.0	100.0	100.0	100.0	100.0	100.0	100.0

[a] Based on Social Security sample data. [b] Excluding farm employment. [c] Including nonclassified and nonclassifiable.
Source: Brian Perkins and Dale Hathaway, *The Movement of Labor between Farm and Nonfarm Jobs*, Table 8A.

Mention already has been made of the high back movement of persons who had moved from farm to nonfarm employment. Even in years of low unemployment such back movement appears to be surprisingly high. This raises questions as to the reasons for such reverse mobility. One obvious explanation would be that persons who left farm employment found that they made less in nonfarm employment than they had in agricultural employment. An indication that adverse economic experience in the nonfarm labor market is a strong factor in back movement into the farm labor force is shown in Table 9. It ap-

Table 9 Income Differentials of Off-Farm Movers by Type of Coverage in the Year Following the Mobility Period: 1955–56, 1956–57, and 1957–58 [a]

(In Dollars)

Mobility Period	*Persons Who Were Farm Employed in Both Years of the Mobility Period* (*$*)	*Type of Coverage of Movers in Year Following Mobility Period:* *Nonfarm Sector* (*$*)	*Farm Sector* (*$*)
1955–56			
Median income in 1955	1,287	1,295	1,305
Median income in 1956	1,480	1,942	1,284
Differential of median incomes [b]	+193	+647	−21
Mean income differential [c]	—	+438	−75
1956–57			
Median income in 1956	1,429	1,367	1,542
Median income in 1957	1,468	1,766	1,205
Differential of median incomes [b]	+39	+399	−337
Mean income differential [c]	—	+295	−228
1957–58			
Median income in 1957	1,448	1,484	1,697
Median income in 1958	1,600	1,654	1,256
Differential of median incomes [b]	+152	+170	−441
Mean income differential [c]	—	+131	−305

[a] Computed from Social Security sample data.

[b] Equal to the median income of the group in the second year less its median income in the first year of the period.

[c] Equal to the simple average of the measured income differentials of the individuals in the group.

pears that persons who left farm employment and remained in nonfarm employment were those who experienced rather significant income gains from this occupational mobility. The average gains were larger during years of high employment. On the other hand, those who left farming and then returned to farm employment after a year of nonfarm employment experienced a decline in income in their nonfarm employment, on the average. Moreover, if the year they left farming was a year of high nonfarm unemployment the average income losses were relatively large, apparently large enough to induce a return to the farm work force.

The lower earnings of those who returned to farming seem to have been the result both of less off-farm employment and of rates of pay lower than were received by those who remained in their nonfarm jobs. Examination of Social Security data indicates that the back movers had fewer quarters of covered employment than those whose occupational mobility was more permanent and the back movers had a significantly lower income per quarter of covered employment.

Several personal characteristics of the back movers are significant. First those returning to agriculture contained a much higher proportion of farm operators than was true of the original outmovers, indicating that either farm operators are less successful in occupational mobility than hired farm laborers or that, given an adverse nonfarm experience, farm operators more frequently have some place to go back to in agriculture.

Back movers tended to be older than the average of those participating in occupational mobility, again indicating the adverse selectivity of the present labor market toward older workers. The rate of back movement did not appear to be related to the race of the individual.

The regional effects of the back movement into the farm labor force were of some importance. Some regions, the Northeast and Pacific, continued to experience a net out-migration from the farm labor force despite the rise in nonfarm unemployment in 1958. In the West North Central and South there was a large back movement, especially of farm operators in the South. This raises an interesting question: Why did the South experience the most adverse situation relative to back movement into farm employment during a recession which was heavily concentrated in durable goods manufacturing outside the area? [20]

We can deduce that this was the result of three factors. First, farm workers in the South and West North Central regions are more likely to have to migrate physically in order to enter nonfarm work than in other regions. Local labor markets clearly offer fewer opportunities in the South than in other regions.[21] Second, those who leave agricultural employment tend to go to industries which are subject to cyclical as well as secular downturns in employment. Finally, such persons tend to be marginal in the nonfarm industries and thus are subject to layoff when labor force reductions occur. It is not surprising, then, to find that it was the South, where the local unemployment rates were lower than average for the nation, which experienced the greatest backflow into farm employment during the recession. Because of the relatively low level of skills and of education that prevail among the Southern farm work force they are likely to suffer the most adverse effects in the modern labor market even when the major causes are located in other regions.

In general, while occupational mobility from the farm labor force is high, the labor market does not work satisfactorily for farm people attempting to find nonfarm employment. Many who leave the farm work force return to it, probably as the result of adverse income experience. Farm people clearly are not achieving a wide diffusion in the total nonfarm labor market when they do leave agriculture. Instead, most of them end up in lower-paying, less promising occupations in the nonfarm economy, and in the contracting rather than the expanding industries insofar as labor force is concerned.

Farm people have been handicapped in leaving farm employment for several generations by their generally fewer years of formal education and by the lower quality of that education. Moreover, this handicap is greatest in the age group 25 to 45, where occupational mobility

[20] Total employment declined by about 1.5 million from 1957 to 1958 (ave.), and employment in durable goods manufacturing declined 1.0 million. (Economic Report of the President, January 1962, Table B.-24, p. 236.)

[21] W. Keith Bryant, *An Analysis of Inter-Community Income Differentials in Agriculture in the United States.*

is most probable if it is to occur at all.[22] If greater occupational mobility out of agriculture is going to occur for farm workers over 25 it probably will require special policies to offset the adverse selectivity of the present labor market toward such persons.

IMPLICATIONS FOR POLICY

In the aggregate the transfer of persons from the farm work force to nonfarm employment has appeared rapid to most people. Yet underlying this rapid reduction in the farm work force there is ample evidence of frequent frustrations, disappointments, and financial losses for large numbers of farm people. No one would suggest that all the frustrations and disappointments of life can and should be removed by public policy, but certainly a society with the resources of ours can do more than is now being done to achieve mobility out of those occupations where technical advance (which vastly benefits all society) is putting tremendous economic and social pressure for greater occupational mobility.

On the issue of full employment there can be no argument at this point in time. It is a necessary prerequisite for greater occupational mobility from the farm labor force. Perhaps the greatest need for recognition of this fact is among farm people themselves, whose representatives often are among those most opposed to policies that will expand employment.

The widespread use of multiple job holding as a way out of agriculture suggests several needs. One need is for much better occupational testing and counseling for those interested in occupational mobility. The high rate of entry into industries with a stable or declining labor force would also suggest need for further counseling. Multiple job

[22] The difference in median years of school completed between white rural farm and urban males ran as follows in 1960: Total 25 years and over 2.5 years; 25–29 years old 0.4 year; 30–34 years old 1.4 years, 35 to 39 years old 1.8 years; 40 to 44 years old 2.9 years; 45 to 49 years old 2.5 years; 50 to 54 years old 1.8 years; 55 to 59 years old 0.7 year; 60 to 64 years old 0.5 year. Source: Dale E. Hathaway, J. Allan Beegle, and W. Keith Bryant, *Rural America,* Chapter 6, Table 6-4, to be published in 1966.

holding and the high rate of back-movement also suggest the need for greater income security for those engaged in occupational mobility. Until the rate of adverse experience declines substantially we can hardly blame farm people for keeping some contact with agriculture until they feel securely situated somewhere else.

The issue of training or retraining for occupational mobility is always present. Such training costs generally will not be borne by the first nonfarm employer since, once achieved, they become part of the skills of the individual trainee and cannot be captured by the employer. Therefore, it has been generally assumed that such training should be the direct function of a public agency. This is questionable. Another approach would be a public subsidy to cover the cost incurred by the trainee in a private company. Obviously, one of the barriers to occupational mobility is that the marginal value product of the new entrant is less than his cost to the employer until he has acquired the necessary skills to perform effectively in his new job. As minimum wages increase, this gap may become so high that no industry can afford to hire an unskilled worker. This will push more and more of the needed occupational training back into an already overburdened educational system and will preclude occupational mobility for many persons who for age or other reasons are unable to return to the formal educational system.

Another advantage of the subsidized in-place training would be that the individuals would have work experience as well as training. As any teacher knows, the two are not the same, and both are needed. Moreover, such a system would reduce placement problems appreciably, which often are major even with well-trained individuals.

Most of my suggestions are aimed at improving the chances of successful occupational mobility out of farming. The gross rate of movement need not be increased in order to sharply increase the net rate of out-movement from farming. I suspect, however, that if the chances for successful out-movement from the farm labor force were improved the lure of agricultural life might prove very weak for many now earning less than $1,000 per year as a farm wage worker or the operator of an uneconomic farm.

[6]

Farm Manpower Policy

VARDEN FULLER

FARM MANPOWER POLICY VERSUS NATIONAL MANPOWER POLICY: A HISTORY OF ALIENATION

That we have serious and broad deficiencies in farm manpower policy is not a startling new discovery, nor are these deficiencies attributable to lack of knowledge. Although farm labor and related matters of rural poverty and underemployment have never been highly glamorous areas of research, agricultural economists and rural sociologists, both in government and in academic institutions, have sustained an interest and a commendable level of research activity in these areas. From these efforts, policy makers have had within their grasp fully substantiated evidence on several pervasive problems: (1) that very large proportions of farms have been too small to offer full employment to the farm family, and that technological advance was resulting in many of these small inadequate farms at the same time that the number of adequate commercial farms was increasing; (2) that with sustained and rapid technological advance, labor requirements were rapidly declining, thereby creating intense pressure for mobility and occupational adjustment; (3) that farm people are highly mobile and have migrated in magnitudes historically unparalleled; (4) that the process of migration was draining away the most productive age categories and, even so, frequently resulted in considerable hardship to the migrant because of his lack of information and preparation for other work; (5) that particular segments of American agriculture continued to depend upon obtaining the services of a very large popu-

---

VARDEN FULLER is Professor of Agricultural Economics, University of California, Berkeley.

lation of seasonal and migratory workers for whom sufficient employment to gain an acceptable livelihood was not available.

By emphasizing that we have had knowledge which has gone largely unutilized I do not wish to imply that our policy deficiencies have been attributable to perversity or ill will on the part of policy makers and administrators. Rather, it seems more realistic to find the policy obstructions in the structure of political forces and in ambivalences associated therewith.

In this country it has never been clearly decided whether agriculture is a regular occupational category and therefore subject to the regimen of being examined in labor force terms. It is not a foible of statisticians that employment statistics are reported in the nonagricultural, agricultural dichotomy. Whether we regard the historic model of the yeoman family farmer as being a transformation of European peasantry or not, it is true that the thinking about farm people has run somewhat parallel in the sense that until quite recently farm people and their economic activities were regarded as being somewhat apart from national occupational structures. Neither for the European peasant nor for the American farmer was the concept of income parity (as a reciprocal of manpower adjustment) a relevant concept until recently. We share with other industrial countries the evolution of the philosophy—with some backing in explicit policy—that farmers should have incomes equal to those that prevail in comparable occupational categories, but Americans have not yet gone that far with respect to hired farm workers.

Ambivalences of perception do not survive except in a political context that is favorable to their survival. In the few years in which we have begun to look on farm labor through a manpower focus, the relevant political public might be classified in three ways: (1) those adversely affected by the lack of affirmative manpower policy, including farm families pushed into migration, those with insufficient resources, and those who have tried to make a living as seasonal and migratory wage workers; (2) those who benefited from the adversity of the prior group and those not adversely affected by the absence of an affirmative manpower policy, including employers of hired farm labor, those who were interested in obtaining additional land for farm enlargement, and those who saw a political advantage in having farm income statistics attenuated through the inclusion of low income units; (3) the indifferent or confused general public.

Political power has been highly concentrated in the second category, that is, those not adversely affected by an impassive-negative farm manpower policy. It is they who have had organizational articulation and the ability to employ ideological manipulation in the interest of perpetuating ambiguities. In this environment the latitude of discretion available to legislators and administrators has been sharply constrained, both as to policy development and as to prosecution of program under existing authorities.

The nation has had important policies and programs that initially were affirmative to farm manpower. Foremost among them were the liberal land policies embraced in the Homestead Act and related legislation, the Reclamation Law which subsidized the development of farm land, and the experimental-educational structure of the land-grant college system which accelerated the advancement of production technology. When the accumulated impacts of technological advance became negative to the income position of farmers, under circumstances analyzed by C. E. Bishop in Chapter 1, government had to nullify the productivity it had helped to create by instituting production controls, including the subsidizing of the idleness of a considerable part of the nation's most productive acreage under the Soil Bank and related legislation. In retrospect we may now observe certain eccentricities in American political capabilities. Finding ourselves in the dilemma of having expanded our agricultural capability too rapidly and therefore being confronted with surpluses, we have reacted legislatively by retiring excess land under full compensation and retiring excess farm people into an oblivion of no pay, and until quite recently with very little concern for their welfare.

For hired farm labor our legislative response has been even more explicitly negative. In the New Deal era Congress passed a series of labor acts—Fair Labor Standards, Social Security, Unemployment Insurance and Labor Relations—from which hired farm labor was systematically excluded. Subsequently, after the World War II emergency the Secretary of Labor accepted a mandate from farm employer organizations to create a separate, identifiable farm placement service as a condition of having this function restored to the Department of Labor from the War Food Administration. Finally there came the ultimate in alienation of farm labor when in 1951, under the guise of the Korean War emergency, organized farm employer interests obtained the passage of Public Law 78, which put the United States Government, and specifically the Secretary of Labor, into the position of being an agent to procure temporary farm labor (from Mexico) on terms already discordant with prevailing American labor standards and destined to become even more so under the latitude of collusive action allowed farm employer interests.

With the majority of the general electorate hopelessly paralyzed in confusion while the minority divided its support prolabor and promanagement on sentimental and affiliative grounds, farm labor issues and problems have seldom achieved the status of respectable debate. Only in the contemporary context of a broad national concern about poverty and unemployment in general does the situation of the less privileged in agriculture begin to emerge from the bounds of narrow agrarian equity argumentation.

In the restricted sense of eliminating redundant labor from farms, the essentially laissez-faire policy of past decades has already done much of the job. As a version of history, it has become fashionable to look upon this export of labor as an agricultural contribution to economic growth. Such a contribution it has been, but as a windfall. Since the technological revolution was virtually an autonomous force generated out of scientific advance and not deliberately designed toward the objective of releasing farm workers, it is better history to acknowledge that, without the blessing of a highly favorable nonfarm employment climate, technological advance and an impassive employment policy would have been on collision course.

As the residual of farm population has declined in magnitude, its composition has also shifted toward older age categories and toward a sharply diminished rate of natural increase. The potential of migration is sharply decreased for both the immediate and the distant future. Given this outlook, we might be tempted to the conclusion that an affirmative policy for farm manpower is no longer a matter of great urgency, that the portable component of the population and its associated problems have already been exported or will take care of themselves, and that the immobile component—based largely on what Reverend Weller [1] calls "Yesterday's People"—are as well off in their current situations as they would be in any other that could be made available to them. If in considering this question we are thinking in terms of a manpower policy particularized to farming, I would be doubtful; but if our thinking is in terms of affirmative actions to bring farm people and their occupations into the orbit of national manpower policy, then I believe that the only reasonable choice is to do so.

Although remnants of Jeffersonian agrarian philosophy still survive, they no longer have political significance. Whether deliberately or by default, most of the turning points other than those in labor standards that commit farming to be a component of the industrial society have already been passed. What remains to be done are some finishing and polishing of occupational status within commercial farming and the clarification of complementary employment relations between commercial farming, noncommercial farming, and other rural industries.

INTEGRATING FARM AND NATIONAL MANPOWER POLICY

If the proposition is accepted that the manpower policy appropriate for agriculture should not in objective be different from national manpower policy, several areas for development are indicated. These fall basically into three categories. The first is the removal of a series of statutory discriminations incurred in the 1930s against farm workers. The second is a category of particular efforts by agencies to extend to farm people the educational, training, and antipoverty program benefits for which they are eligible but which are not easily made available to them because of remoteness, lack of information, and motivation. The third category of actions, which should be given considerable stress, has a broad environmental relation to the more specific manpower programs; it is the development of a more diversified, more rationalized, and firmer employment base in rural communities.

[1] "Is There a Future for Yesterday's People?" *Saturday Review,* October 16, 1965, pp. 33–36.

In this connection I shall promote the belief that farm people undergoing occupational adjustment, and others as well, should have choices other than the uncertain ones of moving into congested metropolitan centers. Correlatively, national and local government leaders should be concerned about amenities and the incurring of metropolitan congestion costs, while also in some rural areas incurring the costs of depopulation. Finally, I will make the argument that the development of the rural nonfarm economy has suffered from political neglect and unimaginative conception.

Eliminating Statutory Discriminations against Hired Farm Workers. In the legislative proceedings on fair labor standards, unemployment insurance, social security, and labor relations much emphasis was given to the particular characteristics of farm employment. Attention was centered around the image of the working farm family assisted by the hired man who, after gaining experience and saving money, would advance up the ladder to a farm of his own. It was an idealized rich human relationship of pronounced congeniality and fraternity, one clearly not to be tampered with by regulations and legal constraints.

For the incidental seasonal and temporary hired help there were the burdens of having to keep formal payroll records, of having to make detailed reports on wages, hours, and earnings, and of having enforcement agents poking into the family business. Given the prevailing image of the family farm as a reference concept, the equity matter seemed direct and simple. If burdens and costs were to be imposed by law, they would fall directly on the farm family, which typically and on the average was too poor to absorb any additional burdens. Consequently, since no other interest organization was present to challenge the validity and universality of the family farm model, the a priori case for total exclusion of farm labor was quite readily established.

In specific detail, some telling objections could be raised against minimum wages, unemployment insurance, and unionization for farm workers. These objections were generally similar to or parallel with counterpart objections made against any programs at all; but in the particular environment of agricultural employment they had greater poignancy. The national minimum wage would have struck hard in low-wage southern agriculture; short-term, seasonal hiring made it difficult to apply the insurance principle of unemployment insurance; perishable crops and livestock were vulnerable if unionization were to result in effective strikes.

Nevertheless from the legislative record we may reasonably infer that the ability of Congress to find validity in these kinds of arguments was closely correlated with the presence or absence of countervailing political power. Had there been a greater balance of interests, legislative attention would likely have turned from thoughts of exclusion to thoughts about the possibilities of resolution, adaptation, and accommodation.

The contemporary political environment in which these exclusions of farm labor may be reconsidered is quite different from the one that prevailed in the New Deal days. Because of the broad interest in unemployment, poverty, and underprivilege, substantial support from outside the farm worker population may now be expected. Whereas in the 1930s the issues between farm employers and hired farm workers were seen in rather restricted personal and equity terms, these same issues now would likely be seen and resolved in a broader context and one embracing the rights of individuals in industrial democracy and self-determination.

Even so, with reference to the removal of agriculture from the national minimum wage (which is the only item in this category currently being proposed) some of the old arguments are still being made. The principal contention is that under a mandatory higher wage much of the employment of hand labor will be discontinued and the work will be done by machines. There is unquestionably much validity in this contention; further mechanization is likely in any event but under wage pressure it would be accelerated.

Because there are no effective barriers to entry into farm jobs there is no question but that agriculture offers opportunities to low-productivity individuals in work that does not have a high value. In a somewhat obscure way, temporary farm work is as much conjuncture of unsolved social and economic problems as it is an employment category. The cause and effect relationships that appear in this conjuncture are sometimes confusing. When the workers are found to be poor or destitute, farm wages and employment conditions are often blamed. Actually, the cause and effect relationship, at least initially at the time of entry into farm work, may be more the other way. Although farm workers may not have *become* poor from working in agriculture, they have become agricultural workers because they were already poor. Thus in the sense of providing an opportunity for those not accepted elsewhere, temporary farm work may be regarded as ameliorating poverty rather than causing it. Moreover, many individuals and groups have made their way through temporary farm employment and into more acceptable situations in agriculture and elsewhere. Hence it has not been entirely a dead end.

Nevertheless, the maintaining of a segment of quasi-employment in agriculture is the counterpart of the ancient cottage industry system and has the same propensity to disguise a backlog of unsolved social problems. If we were to imagine the situation in which problems of technological displacement, discrimination in employment, old age, mental and physical health, vocational rehabilitation, and education were all solved we would be imagining a situation in which very few persons would be available for seasonal farm work. It seems most dubious that society does well by individuals who have the potential of productivity and self-dependence and whose needs are therapeutic and rehabilitative if it preserves arrangements which obscure these potentialities and needs.

Extension of the national minimum wage will be a step toward clearing away this agricultural quasi-employment obscurity, but it cannot do the complete job. The therapeutic and rehabilitative measures available through the current manpower training, employment, and anti-poverty programs—all of which should decrease the ameliorative dependence on farm work—will have to bear the major burden.

And beyond the prospective results of these measures there is a pervasive problem which may survive, which is the persistent downward pressure on factor earnings of labor, both self-employed and hired. Bishop dealt with some aspects of this situation in the first chapter, but some additional comments need to be made.

Wage rates paid to hired labor and earnings of self-employed labor have both been persistently low. Some explanations have been offered, but they are shrouded in obscurity partly because of the general issues of farm depression, government policy, and ability to pay. As both self-employed and hired farm people have some mobility and could presumably leave, we are impelled to the conclusion that the implicit supply price of labor to agriculture is peculiarly different. For seasonal and migratory hired workers there is the recharging residual supply—freedom of entry explanation which approaches being a sufficient one. But this does not account for the persistence of low returns to the self-employed, whose numbers have declined sharply the last quarter century.

In my view the downward pressure on labor earnings derives initially from the particular attributes of the farm enterprise. There are large-scale farms in which the functions of manager and worker are clearly separated. In national proportions these farms are a small minority, but in areas of concentration, particularly in California, their numbers are more than incidental and their share of output is impressive. Nevertheless, the implicit model quite subconsciously employed for policy thinking and in the application of political perspective is the family farm enterprise, the essence of which is self-employment, self-management, and self-capitalization, and in which hired farm labor is supplemental and incidental. Self-employment of farm operator and family members accounts for approximately 70 percent of the hours worked in the nation's agriculture.

For reasons that are difficult to explain in other than historical and ideological terms, American farmers have established a behavior pattern giving primary emphasis to their roles as land owner and capitalist; they have little regard for the roles of themselves and members of their families as self-employed laborers. The empirical evidence for this conclusion and the mechanism through which it is made operative are the market for land and the relationship between land values and farm income.

Since 1950 aggregate realized agricultural income has remained substantially constant in current dollar terms. In this time farm population has declined by one-half and total man-hours used in agriculture by approximately two-fifths. Under these circumstances, according to classical economic theory, the a priori expectation would be that the value of land should fall and the value of labor should rise. But in American agriculture the classical logic has been inverted, for the residual claimant is not land but labor. Accordingly, during these years the level of labor returns has changed very little, but the capitalization of farm land has doubled.

In effect, the benefit of labor-saving technological advances has been fully absorbed into land values. If land inflation had not occurred, the total dollar residual for labor would have been substantially constant through 1950–62; consequently, as man-hours of labor declined the earnings per hour could have significantly increased. In 1962 the inflated value demands of land after 1949 were in effect costing something like 36 cents per hour of labor earning.[2]

Farm price-support programs, which characteristically have their eligibility embedded in land and its production history, contribute to this situation. By their behavior in land markets, farmers have demonstrated that they are quite prepared to sacrifice current labor income in the competition to acquire land. Their behavior appears to be built on the expectation that land inflation will continue indefinitely and that they will be able to realize compensatory income in capital gains.

It is quite apparent that in such a system of wage determination, full integration with the national wage structure will be difficult, because in the national system wage determination emerges from much more clearly separated roles of labor, management, and investment.

Less than full employment is a deep affliction of the farm work force. Yet the aphorism has validity that what farm workers need is not unemployment insurance but more work. Admittedly, an insurance approach with tax premiums based on the expectation of continued employment is not a satisfactory way to cope with a situation in which underemployment and unemployment in magnitude are the normal expectation. Nevertheless, the needs are not met by the aphorism; nor were they met by categorical exclusion.

The inherently biological peaks of seasonal activity are likely to remain an intractable problem. The initial impact of technological change was to aggravate this situation. This happened because peak seasonal hand-labor tasks, especially in the harvesting of fruits and

[2] More details are contained in a statement prepared by the writer for the Senate Committee on Agriculture and Forestry which appeared in the *Congressional Record,* April 1, 1965, p. A1579.

vegetables, were left exposed after other tasks that had offered complementary employment were mechanized or transferred off the farm. The residual employment on the individual farm and in the area was shorter in term and therefore less attractive to persons seeking continuous employment. Moreover, the mechanization of some tasks in advance of others has also left exposed situations, as in the instance of cotton and grapes in California.

After mechanization of hand and stoop labor tasks, most of the strife and hardship in the particular crop have seemed to disappear, although some of the work remaining still involves temporary seasonal employment.

Except for the mechanization of hand tasks, approaches to minimizing the impacts of seasonality have been mainly unfruitful exhortations. It has been declared that farmers should diversify their crops and livestock in order to have a more continuous demand for labor. Or, alternatively, if individual farms were to be specialized in crops having peak labor needs, diversification should occur within the area. As most farming areas already have some diversification and some complementarity in seasonality, it has been proposed that there be central pooling of various labor needs, thereby enabling more continuous employment of workers who would shift systematically from one crop to another. This arrangement proved to be effective with Mexican Nationals, British West Indians, and Puerto Ricans under contract but has been less successful when no contractual relations existed.

Still another proposal occasionally made is that public employment be programmed counterseasonally, or that counterseasonal industries be encouraged to locate in farming areas.

That these various propositions have a record of failure (other than in the instances of pooling programs for contract foreign and Puerto Rican labor) is perhaps sufficiently explained by the unfolding of experience. The farmers got their work done without it; there was not enough pressure upon them or upon government officials to motivate action.

I see no harm in letting unemployment insurance do what it can, especially for the more regularly employed farm hands whose situation is about as the Act contemplates. For the remainder of the less than full employment problem of both self-employed and hired workers, the main reliance will have to be upon occupational adjustment through training and mobility and upon the development of complementary seasonal employment in a diversified rural economy.

Exclusion of hired farm labor from the representation election and unfair labor practice provisions of the Labor-Management Relations (Taft-Hartley) Act in 1947 was an exercise of unilateral power by farm organizations. Unlike minimum wages and unemployment insurance, on which plausible if not necessarily inherently compelling arguments against coverage could be made, the case against labor relations had to rest on political power augmented only by broadly shared anti-union sentiments.

Given the characteristics of farm employment and the composition of the labor force, the obstacles to unionization are formidable even under the protection of the Act; other peculiar and particular obstacles (such as determination of the appropriate bargaining unit) would stand in the way of effective collective bargaining even if unionization were attained. Consequently, eligibility for the moderate aids available under the Act does not guarantee unionization or collective bargaining, and in my view it is quite possible that there would now be not much more of either if coverage had existed since 1947.

Nevertheless, there is something peculiarly diabolical in the discriminatory denial of aids to self-determination to a population segment most in need of them. Moreover, there have been numerous chaotic strike situations (as this is being written, there is one in grape picking in the Delano district of the San Joaquin Valley of California) in which a determination of representation under the official rules and procedures of the National Labor Relations Board ought to be a benefit to the parties immediately concerned and surely would be helpful to the community at large, including especially those officials charged with keeping the peace.

Particular Efforts to Extend Vocational Education Training and Mobility Assistance to Farm People. In contrast to the discriminatory exclusion of farm people from the labor statutes of the 1930s, farm people are fully eligible to participate in the contemporary education, manpower, anti-poverty, and community development programs. The problems lie in organizing projects and developing participation.

These contemporary programs are of the "outreach" type in the sense that they depend upon initiative being taken by local governments and local community leaders for the utilization of the technical assistance and appropriations centering in federal government. Consequently, these programs are vulnerable to the influence of entrenched powers and interests, which may prevent significant projects from getting started.

This vulnerability is particularly great in rural areas because of the inarticulateness of sparsely scattered people who might be potential participants as against influential commercial farmers who may disfavor projects which imply the prospects of reducing their labor supplies. Even if the local power structure may be affirmative to a particular project there remain the difficulties inherent in a widely scattered, not well-informed, potential clientele.

As C. C. Aller reports in Chapter 7, the Department of Labor is putting considerable emphasis on its experimental and development projects and on new arrangements including vocational training centers to extend training programs into the rural sector. The early results of the current training and mobility projects are not yet conclusive, but they do indicate promise and potential as well as the necessity for program personnel to acquire experience on tactical approaches and arrangements.

In programs that depend so heavily upon local initiative there are several aspects of public administration that become critical. Two of these relate to the field organizations which function between federal authority (program supply) and local clientele (program demand). Will the efforts of these agencies be coordinated and articulated or duplicated and diverse? How much constraint will come to bear upon local representatives of federal agencies by reason of political commitments to local power leadership?

The two most directly relevant general agencies which have outreach facilities are the agricultural extension service, whose function is primarily agricultural education, and the employment service structure of the Department of Labor, which has specific program responsibilities in national manpower activities. Out of their respective backgrounds each of these organizations has acquired political alliances with commercial farming and with the leadership of farm organizations which tend to constrain them with respect to other sectors of rural communities.

In these circumstances there are several possible alternatives: (1) Amend the legislation to provide selective program authority and direct line agencies. (2) Create a new rural affairs agency or department to coordinate and proliferate currently authorized programs. (3) Endeavor to achieve maximum performance from the agencies already existing. For reasons which will be enlarged upon, the third alternative has practicality and also possibly enough potential to warrant being given a reasonably extended trial period.

Concluding Comment on Labor Policy Integration. Until 1964 congressional action consistently supported an ever-widening gap between standards for labor in agriculture as against those in other major industrial sectors of the economy. In 1964 the Congress took a significant step in reversing this direction when the authority for administrative action in contracting Mexican Nationals for farm labor under Public Law 78 was not extended. Statutorily, this amounted to allowing the termination of a temporary war emergency measure enacted in 1951 and subsequently renewed several times. Secretary of Labor Wirtz quite correctly interpreted the congressional position as constituting a policy declaration that agriculture should no longer have an exotic labor supply but should obtain its workers from domestic sources and from internal labor markets. Nevertheless, during 1965 incredible demands were made upon the Secretary of Labor to utilize executive discretion in nullification of legislative policy. In standing firmly and resourcefully against these pressures Secretary Wirtz has secured the congressional step and has taken a giant stride on the transitional route to integrating farm manpower into national manpower policy.

DIVERSIFICATION AND DEVELOPMENT OF THE RURAL ECONOMY AS A SUPPLEMENT TO MANPOWER POLICY

Inherently the primary object of manpower policy is to promote individual occupational ability and self-dependence. For those who accept the proposition previously outlined, the object of farm manpower policy is to equalize the opportunity for achieving the above ends as between those associated with agriculture and all others. Yet, as Dr. Tolley finds, the years to come will probably see ever less need and opportunity in farming. If so, does this imply that surplus farm people will have to continue to move to the cities even if prospects there are far from certain?

In the prevailing thought pattern, developed against a background of an urban versus a rural-farm model, the impassive response to this question is almost certain to be affirmative, but I believe that this propensity to a dichotomistic view should be sharply examined.

As the substance of this section will be largely argumentative, it may as well begin with an allegation: Because political and scholarly attention has been polarized on the complex problems of the metropolitan centers, and in the rural scene upon the price and income problems of the commercial farmer, the rural nonfarm sector of the economy has been neglected. Except for noting the untidiness of urban sprawl, we have scarcely been aware that the decline in the farm population has been offset by an increase in the rural nonfarm population. Where rural depopulation has been evident there has been concern about maintaining the service infrastructure. Much has been said and much written about decentralization of industry, regional development, and community development. There has been an agency structure for the promotion of rural area development through the USDA and ARA. It would, however, be a considerable exaggeration to claim that the rural nonfarm population has received consideration in proportion to either the city or the farm populations.

A number of factors could well have produced a greater interest in rural nonfarm matters: (1) nonfarm people have outnumbered farm people in the rural population throughout the postwar years and now are four-to-one; (2) a significant and rising proportion of farm operators have employment off their farms; (3) of the gainfully employed population living on farms, two-fifths in 1960 reported nonfarm occupations; (4) as shown by Bowles, seasonal and migratory farm workers characteristically obtain a considerable portion of their annual employment in nonfarm jobs.

These facts demonstrate the existence of substantial complementarity in the relations between agriculture and other industries as well as considerable individual versatility in transferring between farm and nonfarm occupations. Nevertheless, policy thinking seems to run in rather insulated farm versus nonfarm dichotomous terms.

Admittedly, being optimistic on the potential of a viable diversified rural economy rests more heavily upon imagination than upon evidence. But our thinking about decentralization of economic activities has tended implicitly or explicitly to carry the prefix "industrial." Thinking in terms of a model based on goods manufacturing has imposed serious constraints on our imagination as to the activities that could be as economically carried on in the country as in the metropolitan centers. If the hypothesis is valid that approaches to full employment in the future will depend upon an increasing governmental component primarily centered on services, explorations are in order to find optimum geographic location. Most frequently mentioned is recreation, which is favored by tradition and established practice but has not, I believe, begun to approach its potential. Retirement is a growing and potentially very large "industry" in which rural areas have been variously involved. And finally there are the two very important growth industries: education and health. Is it not reasonable to believe that substantial proportions of the potential expansion in these activities could just as effectively be handled in the country as in the city? If the reckoning unit for costs and benefits is comprehensive enough, the social accounting would include substantial allowances for avoiding the infrastructural costs of congestion in the cities and also some of the burden of maintaining infrastructures for low-density rural populations. And there are some collateral matters such as fresh air and clean water. Furthermore, in accordance with the usual pattern of development, a complementary structure of enterprises for profit could be expected to follow.

Federal initiative, with respect to the development of the agricultural component of rural life through the USDA and the related land-grant college-experiment station-extension structure, enjoys an illustrious history. Political and professional leadership centering in and around agriculture has not been unaware of the far-reaching environmental changes that press for a developmental approach less exclusively focused on the interests and needs of commercial farming. Such a consciousness was embraced in the land-use planning approach of 1938–42; it was explicitly integral to the Rural Development initiatives of the Department of Agriculture in 1956, which subsequently under Secretary Freeman was broadened to the concept of Rural Areas Development, and in 1965 further broadened in name and concept to the Rural Community Development Service.

It is not to be denied that the agencies and institutions centering their activities on agriculture hold a valuable store of knowledge and expertise on the many facets of rural community development. Moreover, from one staff member to the next their personnel probably has a greater interest in community affairs than is manifest. The restraining force lies in the pressures of farm politics which create an overwhelming demand for budget and program in alignment with the interests of commercial farmers.

However, the constraining influence of farm political pressures should not be seen as an insurmountable obstacle to comprehensive rural development. There is evidence that attitudes are changing; farm organization spokesmen are not being so stridently insistent upon an agricultural focus for all agency activities; agricultural agency people are showing interest and imagination in cooperating with the newly created agencies. The new Smaller Communities Program initiated by the Department of Labor is a thrust into the arena of interagency coordination toward the goal of meeting needs in place.

These comments have led to a three-part conclusion: (1) the potential for development of economic diversity in rural areas is greater than has yet been realized; (2) the restraints upon such developments have been mainly political and organizational and are now becoming less repressive; and (3) integral to a manpower policy which seeks to develop individual capacity should be the planning and promotion of opportunities in other than the congested metropolitan areas. The Public Works and Economic Development Act of 1965 is a noteworthy new addition to our policy commitment in this direction, particularly its Titles III and V, authorizing technical assistance, research, and information, and also regional action planning commissions.

I wish to emphasize that in the foregoing remarks I am not supporting any form of nostalgic agrarianism or any concept of "opportunity homesteads." Self-sufficing and subcommercial farm production should be left to those who are affluent enough to afford it. The kind of development which I believe deserves consideration is neo-rural and pluralistic. It is neo-rural in the sense suggested by Wilbur Zelinsky that marked differences in activities, interests, and attitudes need not characterize rural as opposed to urban living in the future, and that the future of the rural community need not be determined by what happens in agriculture.[3] It is pluralistic in the sense outlined by Ginzberg, Hiestand, and Reubens in their book *The Pluralistic Economy,* which offers a perceptive analysis of the interrelatedness in growth among the profit, the not-for-profit, and the government sectors of the economy. In their concluding paragraph,[4] Ginzberg and associates interpret the established directions of change to imply similar expectations and obligations for the future:

> The progress of our economy depends on the efficiency of each of its three sectors—private, nonprofit, and government—and on cooperation and complementary action among them. No sector by itself can provide all of the jobs that will be required by our expanding labor force. The nation has no option but to strive toward the accomplishment of a satisfactory level of employment. A responsible democracy adhering to its tradition and protective of its future will seek to provide jobs for all citizens who are capable of constructive work. Only such a democracy will be able to command the continuing support of its people.

In commending this conclusion I wish to emphasize that amenities as well as economies are to be achieved if in pursuing these objectives we endeavor to provide some latitude of choice between vertical and horizontal living.

[3] See "Changes in the Geographic Patterns of the Rural Population in the United States, 1790–1960," *Geographical Review,* Vol. LII, 1962, pp. 492–524.

[4] See Eli Ginzberg, Dale L. Hiestand, and Beatrice G. Reubens, *The Pluralistic Economy,* McGraw-Hill Book Co., 1965, pp. 217–18.

[7]

Manpower Development Programs for Farm People

CURTIS C. ALLER

Manpower development programs for farm people is a very complex subject, involving all the institutions, processes, and practices through which our society imparts vocational skills and other work-related attributes to people who live or work in rural areas.

To see this subject in perspective, it is important to keep in mind that manpower development is just one of a number of approaches included in the federal government's growing arsenal of manpower programs. The effectiveness of manpower development activities in meeting the needs of workers, communities, and employers depends, in large part, on coordination with these other programs and on progress in other fields of manpower policy. Gradually, the outlines of a comprehensive and cohesive manpower program have been emerging. This involves linking all existing manpower programs, including those in the area of manpower development, into a coordinated effort to solve problems, identifying gaps in existing services, and developing new ways to improve the effectiveness of the processes and mechanisms of the job market. This constructive approach has been stimulated by the establishment of the Manpower Administration in the Department of Labor.

In achieving this approach we have found that the following are some basic elements that deserve consideration for inclusion in an overall program:

CURTIS C. ALLER is Director of the Office of Manpower Policy, Evaluation, and Research in the U.S. Department of Labor. This chapter is based on a paper prepared by Dr. Albert Shostack, whose assistance is gratefully acknowledged.

Act (ARA), Economic Opportunity Act (EOA), and the Vocational Educational Act (VEA), promise more than can be delivered. We should not forget that the size of the target groups is far larger than our present resources can handle. Thus in the face of three million unemployed workers, substantial involuntary part-time employment, and millions of underemployed workers who need upgrading to obtain or retain decent jobs, the MDTA program will be able to reach fewer than 350,000 people this year (1965). This number includes 175,000 institutional trainees, 100,000 to be enrolled in on-the-job training, some 50,000 to be served in experimental or demonstration projects, and much smaller numbers to be involved in labor mobility demonstration projects, employee bonding demonstration projects, and other research-oriented activities.

Similarly, when we consider the millions of rural people who have moved in recent decades from farm to nonfarm pursuits, from farm areas to cities, and from southern agricultural areas to northern and western slums—with virtually no federal government assistance—the fewer than 100,000 rural people served so far under the MDTA and ARA programs seem of small consequence. In fact, early programs to encourage land settlement and population movement, in rural areas, such as the Homestead Act, may represent a more active manpower policy than any of our current operations.

Although I have some official responsibilities in the MDTA program, I do not view its relatively small size as a crippling handicap. Once we understand the limitations on MDTA resources, the need to derive the largest return from the limited inputs available suggests two main program approaches. First, it suggests that the MDTA program should be viewed as a pilot demonstration activity, stressing the development and testing of new approaches, checking ways of solving fundamental problems, and giving leadership on the frontier of the manpower field.

Second, our limited resources suggest that MDTA services should be aimed at people who have the most serious employment and vocational training problems, people who are least able to adjust on their own to the drastic changes occurring in the job market, and who are most likely to be missed by established manpower development and related services. This group would include unskilled workers with low educational attainment, minority group members facing barriers in moving up the occupational ladder, the long-term unemployed, unemployed people moving to urban areas without vocational education or financial resources, and people in chronically depressed areas. By emphasizing assistance to these categories, federal manpower development programs can provide significant economic and social benefits; can help to ease the most severe personal hardships and social and economic tensions; can avoid duplication of state, local government, and private manpower activities; and can generally derive maximum effectiveness from their relatively small-scale resources.

Because of the limitations on our resources, and the need to control and direct them toward the most important activities and long-run objectives, a basic change in MDTA program operations will shortly be put into effect. Up to now, because of the urgent need to set the recently enacted MDTA into motion, proposals for individual training projects have been developed on a local area basis with relatively little coordination or federal direction. Although these projects have been effective in meeting the needs in many local areas, they have made it difficult to provide overall guidance and to achieve a balanced use of resources in the program as a whole. This procedure will give way to a more systematic approach—the establishment of a formal system of national and state planning. The proposed system provides a means for participating state agencies to make their training needs known to the national office in advance of each fiscal year. It also provides for annual national guidelines which will indicate the kinds of workers, industries, occupations, areas, and training approaches that should be emphasized in the coming year's MDTA operations. We expect this kind of advance planning will assure a balanced use of MDTA resources to meet the most urgent needs of problem groups and to test and demonstrate new methods for solving the most difficult manpower problems. It will permit priorities for services to be established in an orderly and systematic manner.

The proposed planning system will permit a careful review of the training needs of farm and rural nonfarm people each year and will help insure the provision of a fair share of the program resources to meet these needs. With the help of national office review of the annual state plans, there should be assurance that farm people with the most difficult training and employment problems are given special emphasis and that they receive training for the most appropriate kinds of job opportunities. The planning system will also include steps to consider the resources available from the "war on poverty" and from other programs, to help effect a coordinated approach to manpower problems.

My central assignment for this conference, however, is to look briefly at the way our new tools have been used and to indicate the directions for further advances. To do this it will be helpful to group the population into several categories which have distinctive needs and institutional arrangements, and to consider these groups one at a time. We will consider first the youngsters who are attending school, and then move on to the unemployed out-of-school youths, farm people who have jobs, unemployed adult workers, and special problem groups.

IN-SCHOOL YOUTH

The first category to be considered are young farm people who are attending school. Perhaps this segment of the farm population receives less attention than it deserves from planners of manpower development programs. This may occur because it is not an immediate problem group. Youths in school do not present immediate questions of joblessness, lack of vocational preparation, symptoms of social disorganization associated with idleness, or other deficiencies that the "problem groups" display. Yet, of course, meeting the manpower development needs of this group is essential for the long-run balance of human resources and manpower requirements, for bringing out the fullest potential of both the individual worker and the overall economy, and for prevention of the serious manpower problems that are already of concern to us. This group is both an opportunity for our future and, more recently, the source of many of our present problems.

Like other youth, young people with farm backgrounds require a good general education as a basic preparation for the kinds of adaptations and adjustments they will face in the changing job market. They require, also, realistic and early guidance toward occupational careers or toward higher education on the basis of a competent evaluation of their aptitudes, interests, and abilities, in the light of expert knowledge of prospective job opportunities. Finally, youngsters who are not going on to higher education should expect their schooling to provide a good technical or other occupational preparation that would fit them for at least beginner jobs in their chosen vocation.

We have certainly not been able to meet these needs for all farm youngsters, and this has contributed to the unemployment and underemployment which some of the youths face later in life. There is a need for new approaches in this fundamental area, so crucial to the condition of the labor force of tomorrow. There are several situations in which government action may be advisable.

First, a very obvious problem that lends itself to solution by government action involves youths who are unable to complete their education because of inadequate financial resources. The solution to this problem is certainly more complicated than a system of grants or scholarships, because complex family and motivation factors may be involved. Nonetheless, the broadening of manpower development programs in this area alone would probably go a long way toward alleviating future manpower problems of greater complexity.

Federal action to help impoverished youths complete school has already made a good start with the Department's Neighborhood Youth Corps (NYC) established under the Economic Opportunity Act. The NYC provides paid work experience and related services to needy youths, between the ages of 16 and 22, who require such assistance to increase their employability, or to help them continue their education. Enrollees are usually paid a minimum of $1.25 an hour for undertaking useful work under the supervision of state, local, or private nonprofit agencies. NYC projects have already been approved for almost 90,000 youths in rural areas. This number represents about one-fifth of all the youths for whom NYC enrollment has been authorized. The great majority of the rural enrollees will be youths in high school who need supplemental earnings to continue their education.

The Economic Opportunity Act, the Higher Education Act of 1965, and other programs provide assistance for needy college students, administered by the Department of Health, Education, and Welfare. The biggest remaining gap in removing financial obstacles to school attendance, therefore, seems to concern younger children, below the age of 16. For some youngsters from poor families, compulsory school attendance laws alone cannot adequately insure exposure to a suitable level of education. We have learned of children who still stay away from school for lack of proper clothing; children who do not attend school because they must help farmworker parents during the harvest season; and children who do not do their best in school because of inadequate diets, heating, or lighting at home.

It would be advisable in manpower development terms to consider ways of helping such youths under 16 meet their school responsibilities. One idea mentioned has been the reduction of the minimum age limit for Neighborhood Youth Corps enrollees, from 16 to perhaps 14. Another possibility might be straight scholarships for some impoverished youngsters without requiring them to do outside work for their money. Alternatively, we can continue to view the young child's school attendance as dependent on the overall resources of the parents, and explore family income supplements such as children's allowances, the so-called negative income tax, and modifications of public assistance procedures.

A second difficult area is the choice of vocations by rural youths who are attending school. In part, this problem of choosing a life's work is shared with nonfarm people. To help them select appropriate courses of education and training, youngsters are encouraged to make some kind of tentative occupational choice years in advance of entering the labor force. Similarly, schools must make choices on the content of their vocational training based on estimates of what skill requirements will look like years in the future. These decisions must be made in the face of rapidly changing technology and manpower needs, with little knowledge of the independent and competing decisions of other youngsters and of other schools. Obviously, manpower development programs must place great emphasis on accurate assessment of future manpower requirements and resources and on competent vocational guidance of in-school youth.

Rural youngsters and their teachers have a special problem in this matter. Since most rural youth have to look to nonfarm jobs as a means of earning a living, they face the most difficult employment and training adjustments. Yet, in spite of the strong efforts of the employment service agencies, notably in the Smaller Communities Program, and of educational authorities to bring services to rural areas, we can be certain that many farm youths face major career decisions without adequate guidance and support. Perhaps we should seek federal assistance to meet a goal, such as competent vocational counseling and evaluation services available to every school-age youth by 1970.

A third problem area, noted by the report of a Panel of Consultants on Vocational Education appointed by the Secretary of Health, Education, and Welfare in 1961, and by other sources, has been the lag in gearing rural school systems to the vocational needs of farm youngsters. Many rural schools have been unable to provide adequate training for a broad spectrum of nonfarm occupations, particularly occupations suitable for those youths who are required to migrate to cities to find work. There have been problems of procuring adequately trained vocational education teachers, expensive up-to-date equipment, and appropriate school plants in rural areas. In some cases, training has continued to be given in traditional agricultural operations, even though most of the students would be unable to put this kind of training to use.

In this field the federal government can well expand its contribution. The federal role is easily justified because the out-migration of rural youth makes it unfair to impose the entire cost of their education on their home area. The Vocational Education Act of 1963 has successfully broadened federal aid for vocational training in local areas by updating the types of vocational training eligible for assistance and by tying the training more realistically to current and anticipated job market needs. Much remains to be done, however.

A promising approach is the development of a network of central vocational training centers capable of preparing rural youths and unemployed adults in a wide range of skilled occupations in which there is reasonable expectation of employment. Such central schools, which could support staffs of highly qualified instructors and the latest technical equipment, would provide a wider range of training for nonfarm occupations, and of higher quality, than the typical local school in rural areas. This idea received strong impetus in connection with administration of the MDTA program, which encountered high costs, questionable quality, and a limited range of training objectives in trying to set up training in some rural low-income areas. The Vocational Education Act of 1963 already provides some assistance to state agencies adopting the area vocational school concept; this program may deserve to be expanded.

The Office of Education of the Department of Health, Education, and Welfare is showing good leadership in the task of reorienting the vocational training emphases of rural schools to the needs of today's job market. The vocational training outlook for the upcoming generation of farm youth is promising. I think that most will have been equipped with the kinds of work skills and other attributes needed to find a productive and secure phase in the work force.

Finally, a fourth problem of relevance to farm youths in school concerns the special needs of some particularly impoverished groups, such as may be found among Negroes in southern agricultural areas, residents of some Appalachian areas, and people of Mexican descent in the Southwest. Adaptation to the demands of the job market for such youngsters often requires more than the level of general education and vocational training available in their local schools. Many of these youngsters require a reorientation of folkways, attitudes, and cultural outlook to prepare them for unfamiliar urban and industrial life. Some grow up unfamiliar with the simpler requirements of the world of work: basic hygiene, how to get about and use the services available in the city, and the discipline of industrial life.

The schools, of course, cannot control the entire environment of the child; the child's subculture, parents, and friends exert powerful influences on him. Nonetheless, a stress by rural schools on the forms of behavior and ways of thought that would help the farm child adapt to life and work in nonfarm environments is strongly suggested. This stress should begin at the earliest possible age; in this sense, Project Head Start is as much a manpower development program as the MDTA itself. I think that the desegregation of schools under the impetus of court decisions and the Civil Rights Act is a most promising development in this respect, in that it will expose increasing numbers of disadvantaged minority group children to the cultural patterns and expectations of the larger society in which they live.

OUT-OF-SCHOOL, UNEMPLOYED YOUTH

I would like to turn now from youngsters in school to youths who have completed or dropped out of school and who are unemployed or substantially underemployed. This area of jobless out-of-school youth is one in which Department of Labor programs can and do play a significant role. Through local offices and mobile units of state employment service agencies affiliated with the Department of Labor, many thousands of rural youth have been tested, evaluated, counseled, and referred to the most appropriate job opportunity or to available government manpower programs. Federally subsidized MDTA and ARA training projects have assisted some rural youth; more than one-third of the MDTA trainees enrolled in rural areas to date have been under 22 years of age. Weekly youth training allowances have helped provide a means of subsistence to young people taking this training. Significantly, the great bulk of the rural youths in MDTA training have been enrolled in classes for nonagricultural occupations, in which job opportunities are better than on farms.

The Department of Labor's Neighborhood Youth Corps program also assists jobless farm youth. Although most enrollees now receiving paid work experience and related services under NYC are attending school, a significant number are participating in full-time work programs for out-of-school youth. Such NYC programs would seem to be of most benefit to youngsters who do not adapt readily to classroom-type training and to regular studies. The President's national beautification program offers many opportunities for employing and training out-of-school NYC enrollees in rural areas.

Apprenticeship is a third youth program of great interest to the Department of Labor. Unfortunately, opportunities for participation in formal apprenticeship programs, as an avenue for training for skilled blue collar jobs, are very limited in rural farm areas. We should consider ways to expand these opportunities for farm youngsters.

There is a need for innovation in developing new forms of government assistance to youths who migrate from the farm to urban areas. Left on their own, many of these youngsters encounter serious personal, social, and economic difficulties. Consideration might be given to setting up staging centers which would be available to counsel the youths and help them make advance work and living arrangements before their departure; youth hostels and reception centers which could provide temporary shelter, recreation services, and emergency allowances for the youths after their arrival in the city; and related measures. Such facilities might alleviate the adjustment problems of many migrating girls and boys and prevent them from getting into trouble or missing good opportunities in their new location.

A big problem for both farm and nonfarm people concerns those youths who cannot adapt to formal schooling or training and who are already showing behavior and attitude problems which interfere with labor force adjustments. This difficult problem plagues our cities and is undoubtedly aggravated by the unaided and uncoordinated movement to cities of masses of farm people with low skill and educational attainment. The Job Corps represents one hopeful approach toward providing the basic environmental changes needed to help problem youths adjust to the demands of regular employment.

Several exploratory projects have been undertaken under the MDTA to prepare prison inmates for decent jobs prior to their impending release, and to assist and train persons on parole. The results of these projects, so far, have been beyond our expectations, and we expect soon to move to a far larger program.

Intensive consideration has also been given by the Manpower Administration to assisting youths with especially difficult employment and training problems at the point where they are examined, tested, and rejected by Selective Service authorities. To date, the emphasis has been on trying to bring Selective Service rejectees into employment offices for evaluation of their employment problems, for competent vocational counseling, and for referral to appropriate services. A further step warranting consideration might be a voluntary training program to remedy educational and training defects for those rejectees who would like to have the opportunity to serve in the Armed Forces.

EMPLOYED WORKERS

A third category of farm people, the workers who are fully employed or who are not severely underemployed and who prefer to remain in their current occupation, also have important needs. Since they present no immediate problem, our tendency might be to overlook their manpower development at this time. But like employed nonfarm workers, these farm people should have opportunities to upgrade and update their skills, to remedy educational deficiencies, to prepare for occupational changes that might occur in the future, and to otherwise improve their knowledge and earnings potential. The wide range of public night schools and other part-time educational facilities found in urban areas is not matched in most farm areas. Certainly, the upgrading and other training programs of large private industrial employers are not found on even very large agricultural establishments. We might well consider, therefore, ways to encourage the development of part-time general education and vocational training facilities for employed people in rural farm areas.

The situation is considerably different for farm operators. The Department of Agriculture has long maintained widespread training facilities for farmers and their families, ranging from homemaking practices to agricultural and construction methods and management. The Extension Service and other agricultural agencies are well-known forms of manpower development.

The MDTA gave special recognition to the needs of small farm operators by permitting members of farm families with annual incomes of less than $1,200 to qualify for weekly living allowances and training. A significant number of people have qualified under this provision.

It is of particular interest to note that MDTA training has been authorized for well over 2,000 individuals for the occupation of farm operator. By the end of September, 1965, about 1,200 were in training or had completed training for this occupation under the MDTA, and others have been trained as farmers under the Area Redevelopment Act. Generally speaking, the participants in these courses are small farm operators whose personal abilities and land resources have potential for future development. They are taught to improve farming practices, adopt the latest methods and equipment, grow new crops, improve management and administrative skills, and otherwise to increase their returns so as to earn an adequate livelihood. Typically, the training programs are meshed with supportive services provided by organizations affiliated with the Department of Agriculture and other agencies in the local area.

A large proportion of the small farmers participating in these training programs are in Puerto Rico. Most other participants are minority racial group members, for example, Indians in Arizona and Montana, nonwhites in Tennessee. Small farmers in several Appalachian areas have been aided. The few programs that have already been completed will be evaluated intensively to see whether this type of training is feasible and whether it can make a place for competent small farm operators in selected segments of the agricultural economy.

UNEMPLOYED FARM WORKERS

Unemployed and substantially underemployed farm workers are my next category for discussion. This is the group which is the main concern of the MDTA program. This category of workers could be subdivided into smaller groups for analysis purposes, distinguishing the needs of small farm operators, unpaid workers who are members of their families, year-round farm hands, and seasonal hired farm workers. For purposes of this paper, however, the group will be discussed as a whole.

Estimates of the participation of rural and farm people in the MDTA program are still rather rough. As many as one out of every five MDTA enrollees lives in rural areas, as defined by the census. This would mean that training and related services have been authorized for about 100,000 to date, including some ARA participants. We know that 7 out of 10 MDTA enrollees in rural areas are males, more than one-third are less than 22 years of age, and 15 percent are in the "older worker" group, 45 or more years old.

Turning to the occupational objectives of the rural enrollees, we find that only 7 percent have been trained for farm occupations. Most of the men have been trained for skilled and semiskilled blue collar jobs, and the women have tended toward clerical, sales, and service jobs. In particular, very few of the younger trainees were enrolled in courses for farm occupations; they were directed to nonagricultural occupations with expanding manpower requirements.

Although relatively few rural enrollees are being trained in agricultural occupations, a substantial proportion of those who previously worked on farms are receiving training in advanced farm skills. Fully half the approximately 11,000 enrollees who reported farm work as their primary occupation are being trained for agricultural jobs.[1] The great bulk (95 percent) of these workers are males; about one-fourth are nonwhite. Most farm workers who have not been assigned to agricultural training are being prepared for skilled and semiskilled blue collar occupations.

All told, only about 15,000 of the half million trainees authorized under MDTA and ARA have been assigned to training for agriculture.[2] The workers selected for farm courses have generally had farm backgrounds, even when agriculture was not their primary job. They are unemployed or underemployed farm people for whom the learning of advanced agricultural skills represents the most advantageous adaptation in the job market. Emphasis has been placed on selecting the kind of applicants who would have difficulty in adapting to nonfarm jobs, moving to urban settings, and undertaking new ways of life and work.

Three out of five of the enrollees preparing for farm occupations had never progressed beyond the eighth grade. Almost 30 percent are 45 or more years old; this is almost triple the proportion of older workers in the MDTA program as a whole. Only 17 percent were youths under 22 years of age, far fewer than in nonfarm MDTA courses. One-fourth of the trainees are nonwhite; others belong to the ethnic or language minority groups. Most of them had very low earn-

[1] Data through September 1, 1965.
[2] Data through September 30, 1965.

ings in their last regular employment before entering the training program; one-third of the nonwhites had earned less than 75 cents per hour. Many of the adult trainees had not held any regular employment in the past at all. For such people, training for steady work on farms in their home areas may be of the greatest long-term benefit.

The agricultural occupations for which training is being provided fall into several categories. The largest category, about 55 percent of the total, consists of the relatively skilled farm occupations—farm equipment operators, dairymen, foremen, tree pruners, and the like. Next in volume, about one-fourth of the total, is training for small farm operators, mentioned previously. An important third category, accounting for slightly less than 20 percent of authorized trainees, consists of jobs that are related to agriculture but involve work in an urban or nonfarm setting. These jobs include, for example, nursery attendants, park caretakers, and gardeners. Demand in these occupations is rising. Recently, attention has also been given to training American workers to replace foreign labor on United States farms. A recent example is the negotiation of an on-the-job training project to provide short-term training under MDTA for 500 workers in the Florida citrus harvest.

Where it is advisable to retrain farm people for nonfarm jobs, particularly away from their home area, we have learned that the training is more effective when accompanied by appropriate supportive services tailored to their special needs. For example, this may involve providing housing for migratory farm families near the training site; intensive counseling; training in hygiene, proper food habits, and patterns of acceptable behavior; demonstration of the use of modern appliances; arrangements for a flexible training schedule adapted to variations in seasonal labor requirements; individual tutoring; and remedial education. For some workers, training involves a transition from outdoor to indoor work, from active labor to sedentary activity, and from the use of heavy tools to the use of delicate instruments. In effect, basic changes in way of life often accompany the occupational training of farm people.

After training, some workers from farm areas need assistance in moving to locations where jobs are available in their new occupation. We have done some preliminary experimental work in assisting such moves by means of labor mobility demonstration projects authorized on a relatively small scale by Section 104 of the MDTA. These projects, involving grants and loans for moving expenses, assistance in arranging employment opportunities, and provision of counseling services will be evaluated and their experience will be utilized to make our assistance for farm people more effective.

There are three areas on which attention may profitably be focused to improve ways of meeting the manpower development needs of unemployed farm workers. First, more attention should be given to coordinating the several program activities now available to assist these workers. A more effective use of our resources would result from coordination of efforts under the MDTA, the Public Works and Economic Development Act of 1965, the basic education and farm worker assistance programs of the Economic Opportunity Act, Community Action Programs under the Economic Opportunity Act, the Department of Agriculture, and other available resources. This is not intended as criticism; most of the programs are practically newborn. We are beginning to explore with these other agencies effective methods of coordination.

Second, we should consider new ways to facilitate the adjustment of farm people who migrate to urban areas. Guidance and staging centers in the farm areas, reception centers in urban areas, specialized forms of financial assistance, and a variety of down-to-earth, bread-and-butter services deserve consideration. I think that our public policy has progressed to the point that the nation is unwilling to accept the social and economic hardships that go along with the haphazard movement of masses of ill-prepared people to urban slums. If we do not bring order to the migration process, and help the individuals underlying the massive statistics, society will pay higher costs in the form of welfare burdens, delinquency, and similar problems.

In the Office of Manpower Policy, Evaluation, and Research the needs of farm people on the move will receive significant attention in expanded research activities, emphasizing basic information needed for planning action programs. An example of what can be done is a specific research project being developed in Washington with a competent nonprofit research organization. This study will effectively analyze the characteristics and experience of recent migrants from rural to urban areas. The migrants will be identified through their children, utilizing the resources of urban school systems. The migrant parents will be interviewed to determine their work and residence histories, employment status, adjustment problems, and training needs. If appropriate, the parents will be referred to public employment service offices for any necessary assistance.

This experimentation with the early identification of rural in-migrants may not only provide a source of information on the characteristics, motivations, and experiences of the in-migrants but may also help to ascertain the kinds of services such people need to avoid becoming welfare cases or members of the hard-core unemployed.

Third, experience with the Neighborhood Youth Corps work experience program for youths indicates the feasibility of undertaking programs of work experience for unemployed adults as well. Such programs may be particularly useful in increasing the employability of jobless farm workers who cannot easily adapt to formal training and who learn best by doing practical tasks. A small-scale work experience program oriented to adults on public welfare rolls is already under way, stimulated by new resources made available by Title V of the Economic Opportunity Act. Extension of this concept as a manpower development tool, rather than a welfare tool, is well worth considering.

SPECIAL PROBLEM GROUPS

The final category of agricultural workers to be mentioned consists of those special groups whose needs cannot be met by generalized programs but who require services tailored to their unusual characteristics and problems; for example, migratory and Indian farm workers. A great deal can be done for these special groups under Title III-B and other sections of the Economic Opportunity Act. The Bureau of Indian Affairs also has programs in the manpower development field.

The most significant contribution of the Manpower Administration to meeting the needs of these special groups has been through experimental and demonstration projects. These so-called E & D projects, undertaken under the MDTA, are used to test or demonstrate new ways of meeting especially difficult manpower needs, of identifying and solving problems, and of assisting particular types of workers who are likely to be covered inadequately by existing manpower development services. Through last June, almost 10,000 disadvantaged rural people received training or other services in these E & D projects.

Typically, the projects are conducted by local governments, nonprofit welfare groups, and community organizations under contract with the Department of Labor. In the projects for rural people, the organizations involved have included land grant colleges, church groups, such as the Migrant Ministry of the National Council of Churches, and national organizations serving impoverished agricultural people.

The emphasis in the experimental projects for rural people has been on developing new ways of reaching and gaining the confidence of disadvantaged groups, new ways of teaching them needed work and social skills, intensive job development efforts, and efforts to meet the total needs of the family and to improve the overall social and cultural setting. E & D projects have included efforts to tailor techniques to meet the special needs of minority group workers and of migrant workers; development of new sources of labor supply to supplant foreign workers on United States farms; development of off-farm job opportunities to provide income in slack seasons; provision of job information, training, and counseling to help farm workers increase their earnings; assistance in moving to new areas where permanent jobs are available; and provision of basic remedial education to help workers qualify for further vocational training. One project, conducted in several scattered areas, tried to determine whether carefully supervised work on farms, associated with preconditioning activities, counseling, and supportive services, can improve the work orientation and attitudes of problem youths from urban areas.

In the 1965 amendments to the MDTA, Congress gave special recognition to the role of E & D projects in spearheading the manpower development program, and it earmarked resources to operate E & D projects. A separate Office of Special Manpower Programs has been set up in the Manpower Administration to handle this type of work, and an advisory board of distinguished experts will soon be established. They will be devoting a substantial amount of attention to meeting the needs of farm people in the program for the coming year (1966).

CONCLUSION

I have touched but briefly on some of the important manpower development needs of our rural population. The problems in this area are very substantial and long standing; the solutions are slow and undramatic. Yet we do know a great deal about what has been happening in agriculture and why. This is clearly revealed in the analyses presented by the other participants in this conference. The task now is to utilize our present knowledge and growing administrative capacity so as to move beyond tokenism toward broad and pervasive solutions.

Because I have emphasized the topic of manpower development programs, I would like to stress again the obvious fact that such programs alone cannot solve all agricultural manpower problems. Manpower development programs should merely be one part of a coordinated approach to the problems of rural people, tied to programs of better distribution and utilization of workers and to improvements in wages and labor standards. In particular, there are two approaches that deserve, in my opinion, immediate consideration for solving key manpower problems.

First, of particular value for seasonal farm workers would be a program to structure the agricultural job market and to decasualize worker-employer relationships. Such a program would attempt to change prevailing patterns of short-term jobs, intermittent employment, migrancy, and casual day-to-day employment relationships. It would seek to modify the specialized institutions of the farm job market, such as the labor contractor system, the crew system, day-haul recruitment, and payment on a piece rate basis. The goal would be more systematic distribution and utilization of farm workers, guarantees of more regular employment and income, and more stable employer-employee relationships through the development of ingenious new institutions and practices. The Annual Worker Plan developed by the Federal-State Employment Service system shows, in a preliminary way, what can be done by creative thinking along these lines. The work of the late Lloyd Fisher,[3] in his book "The Harvest Labor Market," is also suggestive in this area. My own studies on the decasualization of the agricultural industry in Hawaii have convinced me that such bold new approaches are feasible. But if this is to happen it will require, I think, the strategic intervention of the academic community. Both innovative thought and hand research work are necessary.

The second key area to which I would urge earnest attention is the scandalous use of the public welfare system to subsidize employers of agricultural labor. Drawing on the pool of welfare recipients, farm operators are assured of an adequate labor supply when and where needed, simply returning the workers to the relief rolls for storage during lulls in labor needs. The farm operators thus escape the responsibility normally imposed on employers in nonagricultural industries to provide regular employment and adequate earnings, supplemented by unemployment insurance coverage and a variety of fringe benefits, sufficiently attractive to draw and hold a stable work force. At the same time, individual relief recipients are not helped to make long-range adjustments in the job market. Using public assistance in this way, with its high social and human costs, is the antithesis of the human resource development approach that we should be following.

The new wave of government manpower development activities which has emerged over the last few years can be used creatively to bring unemployed and underemployed rural people into the mainstream of the nation's productive life.

[3] Lloyd H. Fisher, *The Harvest Labor Market in California,* Harvard University Press, 1953.

Index